MW00639241

Odes to Our Undoing
Writers Reflecting on Crisis

This collection of writing was conceived of and edited by graduate students in the MFA program at Saint Mary's College, Moraga, California, initially as part of a course taught by Professor Matthew Zapruder in Fall, 2020. Special acknowledgment and great gratitude to Hannah Wohlenberg and Kehinde Badiru, who heroically saw this book through all the editorial and production phases, into this final product. The Saint Mary's College MFA program would like to thank the RiskPress Foundation, and in particular Charlie Pendergast and Kevin Connor for their ongoing support of our students, who have benefited so greatly from their generosity. All proceeds from the sale of this book will go to the scholarship fund of the Saint Mary's College MFA program, which benefits graduate students in need, particularly from underrepresented communities, so that they can pursue their creative educations.

Odes to Our Undoing
Writers Reflecting on Crisis

Edited by:
Liala Zaray
Hannah Wohlenberg
Natalie Dunn
Marrion Johnson
Mikaela Dunitz
Lizette Roman-Johnston
Katie Ziegler
Tanya Castro

RiskPress

Published by RiskPress
100 Wildhorse
Santa Fe, NM 87506
(with the generous cooperation of fmsbw Press, San Francisco, California)

All rights reserved.

Published in the United States of America
Copyright © individual pieces to the authors, 2022

ISBN: 978-0-9848403-9-7

Without limiting the rights under copyright reserved above, no part of this publication (except in the case of brief quotations embodied in critical articles or reviews) may be reproduced, stored in or introduced into a retrieval system, or transmitted, in any form or by any means (electronic, mechanical, photocopying, recording or otherwise), without the prior written permission of both the copyright owner and the above publisher of this book. The scanning, uploading, and distribution of this book via the Internet or via any other means without the permission of the publisher is illegal and punishable by law. Please purchase only authorized electronic editions and do not participate in or encourage electronic piracy of copyrightable materials. Your support of the author's rights is appreciated. For information contact the publisher at pkcp@aol.com, or as shown above.

Front cover image (detail)
Peter Hwoschinsky ©2021
collage on paper, 23" x 34.75"
hwosch@oz.net

Back cover image (detail)
"Nothing Ever Ends"
Alan Saint Clark ©2021
graphic novel title page

Book design:
Charlie Pendergast and Kevin Connor
pkcp@aol.com

Proceeds from all sales of this book will be given to
St. Mary's College, Moraga, California
Masters in Fine Arts, Creative Writing

Table of Contents

Preface

PRIVATE

ISOLATION

PAST

COMMUNITY

Preface

When this project was presented to us, we jumped at the opportunity to collaborate. The theme, title, and the submission guidelines were all ours to create. In September of 2020, like many of the months followed, it was nearly impossible to fight the paralysis of grief, trauma, stress and exhaustion we had been dealt and were consistently dealing with even while planning. In turn, we figured this anthology could serve as a space to invite artists to share any sort of crisis—ranging from those that loom large above us all, to the more singular ones.

In this anthology, various artists engage creatively on what it means to be in crisis, to be forced to fall in love with Zoom, masks and plastic bags, and the windowpane, seeing the world from the inside. You'll find nuances that shift from grief to isolation to loss; dislocation of structures and strictures; family values; love or something that looks like it; cultural and material dislocations; as well as current or historical injustices that are reflective of societies and the values upon which they stand.

The creative outlets in this anthology switch from private to public, past to present. Crisis in the context of a pandemic brings intimacy to things: luminous skies, "each car a semi-private glass-sealed intake room", abstracts, subjects and even distortions and (a)voids — not being able to visit a favorite hair salon, and "many of us go gray without choice." Families, friends, and loved ones take one another's sadness and even tiny joys, absorbing light; forced into tiny or huge apartments that are also the shape of their crisis. They draw strength from one another's uncertainty with the current world and one that existed without awareness.

We thank these authors, from both inside and outside the Saint Mary's College community, for submitting beautiful work. Thanks to them for being kind, gracious, and patient as we brought this to fruition. And we thank them, most of all, for their work. Our reading experience of this work was a wheel of emotions familiar to us in this time of chaos. We hope it brings a sense of community to the forefront.

In Solidarity,

The Editors
February, 2022

Present

from "Shards"
by CAConrad

our
 little
  places
   within
    are not
    dungeons
    remember
    remember
astronomers point
satellites into space
the military points
 them down at us
  the inverse
  relationship between
  love we offer   and
   what we give this on
   and
    off button
     is another
       opportunity
         to believe
          there are
           only two
            choices

this too
must end
 he said
 breathe like you
 read your poems
  what the hell
  does that mean
   then suddenly
 I'm breathing it
   look at our hands
   baked into being
    by a fleeting magic
    bark with dogs to let
     the neighborhood know
    you can go to
    the address
  knock all you want
  no one is there now
    where the exit signs
     are burned out
       the preexisting
         condition is
         not cancer
          but the
          glass of
          polluted
          drinking
           water
    with our pledge

woodpeckers
 make insects
 make themselves
small as possible
 marooned in nucleus
 of another shattered
   discourse your
   burning building
  appears suddenly
  in this poem
   a wall
  collapses
   revealing a line of
  detectives waiting
  to   see   if   the   soul
  is betrayed will
       we still
      believe in
   the body
   Imagine
   the body
   imagine
   us in the
     mouselike
     dream in
       the wall

1

Newly Arranged Appetite
by Tongo Eisen-Martin

Field of grass on the radiator
                    when you played

rhythming razors
hand pulled into an american institutionalization
            dragging a century across a tobacco leaf
            Making the mountain of painkillers a secondary definition

                        but money is green?

you are laying in the hospital for a week thinking about the various distances of love

also the various distances of
what police are actually doing---Mason-Dixon line standing up straight
Brochure of a liquor store on the corner
Identity climate like a karmic stream that goes hexagonal in the sky
Cash crop/You die

                    Seventh street siren inviting you into a paint can
                    Hip hop born already 8 years old in a lotus flower

We just want to know who gave the devil a protection spell

white mask students of the left
sipping hibiscus whisky
European boots masquerading as relationships to trees
Heart-felt education of a modern slave
                                -Scene 3

Kill Kings
Eat Thrones

Consciousness in big Broadway letters
Closing the street to the New York 21

The Atlantic Ocean nearby licking South Carolina like art for the shrine. Like the streets are irrelevant.

Spirit world about Black people
by Black people
on the canvass
and the distance between
the hand and the canvass

You fasten six strings to a spitting Cobra

Your .40 is supportive of all art-making. It's an epoch if the streets say it is. A
junkie stands up for God. It's an instinct of talent. A coup on Seventh.
                                                    -The true meaning of numbers

To organize millions

Like the ruling class have a child (a ticket taker to the wealth)
        The floor map between coal miner and in-crowd is easy to describe
        The challenge is to take all of these imperialist hybrids
        And pen stomp them into an apartment staircase
                                        to yearn for cosmic proof

                                to recruit a soldier every day that you are alive

you start sleeping on the floor with your art… with the vigil world
with a nonchalant horn-personhood
or decent liver for this causality
        stuffing pollution into your pockets
                balancing jewelry on this poem

Peligrosa
by Carol Dorf

> Only at night could my Golem rise from the old futon
> and leave the basement. Once my Golem paused by
> the river – No Access – Peligrosa. A guard dog paced
> behind the gate.
>
> I should have prepared more notes for the Golem,
> said the Sofer.
>
> The Golem can't decide on pronouns. For a while I
> pretended to understand, offered more clay and slip
> to allow for adjustments.
>
> Dreams interrupted by bombs and prisoners – John
> Woo and his brief to justify waterboarding. It is no
> wonder the Golem paced through the night crashing
> into the old statues, warriors that fill the plaza.
>
> On the fourth night a prisoner invented an ally
> much like the Golem with an additional ammunition
> belt. Constellations would have filled the sky but
> floodlights erased all but the crescent moon.
>
> Sometimes my Golem would ask for paper and
> pencil. The words they wrote were incomprehensible
> – stick figures in the margin walked through what
> could have been a moon.

Once my Golem tried to eat, tearing plums off the tree and swallowing them whole. No one commented on the distended belly. Upon encountering the Golem or the prisoner, the witnesses' eyes couldn't blink quickly enough.

After the war, before the Golem lost the word beneath its tongue, the prisoner asked, Tell me the truth – did you know what was happening there? On that night the moon was full, showing not just the outlines of trees but the patterns of their leaves.

Tent of Ambiguous Grief
by Cara Meredith

There's a moment when grief moves into the neighborhood. It pitches a tent in the backyard, its stakes immovable, its walls like a polyester kind of cement. My children play games around it, theirs both a knowing and an oblivion to its presence.

Mama, the tent's taking up a whole lot of space now, I imagine my six-year-old saying. He knows it's there, but he finds a way around it. He zooms his trucks up squishy side walls; he plays hide-and-go-seek beneath flyaway nylon flaps. He learns to avoid its bulky, cavernous shadow, instead, digging holes in a mound of dirt ten feet to the right. Sometimes his awareness is a gift; other times his ignorance feels like sheer overwhelm to me.

I, meanwhile, sit in a camping chair in a corner of the yard. Because this is a rental, we do not purchase patio furniture. We'd like to believe that we will not live in this place forever. We will not be stuck in this house, with its leaky faucets inside and its abundance of pesky rodents outside, for the rest of our days. Someday we will move into our forever-home. Someday we will perhaps dismantle the tent and buy some permanent patio furniture of our own.

This dreaming, of course, is a privilege: an advantage of the now and of what may be in the future. But for now, the tent remains, my dreams halted — for this tent is not actually a tent, but a constant reminder of crisis and of an inescapable kind of grief.

In this moment (which is in fact hypothetical but not all that far from the real truth), what I want is to get out of the chair and join my son in his digging escapades: I will be a fun mom! I will enter into the beauty of the present moment, dirt caking underneath fingernail beds, sun beating down onto the freckles of my neck.

But I do not get up from the chair. I sit and I stare, perhaps at him or perhaps at the Large and Immovable Thing in the backyard which feels impossible and permanent, all at once.

I want to create, to feel the glide of ink streaming from my fingertips, down onto the page. I want to hunker down in my laundry room office, where my laptop, a desk calendar, and a random assortment of books and papers have replaced the table that once held tidy piles of socks and underwear, shirts and shorts. I want to sit in my teal swivel chair, the one that threatens to crash into the washer and dryer if I push away from the grainy wooden table. I want to hole up there, pointer fingers hovering over the "F" and "J" keys, watching as the words move from soul to brain, on over to the screen itself.

I want the magic to return.

But grief seems to have zapped all the creativity inside of me.

I am exhausted, weary, tired to the bone. But I am also tired of feeling tired, tired of feeling like I can't get ahead, tired of feeling the weight of ambiguous loss.

As the psychologists among us have noted, with the pandemic came ambiguous loss for millions across the globe. Normally, ambiguous loss comes in the aftermath of other losses: following a divorce, a parent moves out of the home. Following an Alzheimer's diagnosis, a grandparent fails to recognize his or her grandchild. [1]

With Covid-19, the loss was profound. Not only was there a loss of life as we once knew it, of normalcy and stability and perhaps predictability too, but there was a loss of real human, fleshy life — of more than half a million deaths due to the virus, just in the U.S. alone. Schools and businesses and government offices shut their doors, just as foreclosures and food pantry lines and job losses increased both in presence and in reality. From racial injustice and civil unrest to a divisive political election, kids in cages and unfathomable gun violence, our world upended anew, an ambiguity of the unknown ours for the keeping.

Maybe it was just me, but when ambiguous loss marked every news cycle, every social media update, and every nook and cranny in my utterly boring, everyday life, I couldn't create anymore. I couldn't spit out a coherent sentence, let alone an entire paragraph, essay, or chapter for my next book.

All I could do was sit in the camping chair in the backyard and stare at the metaphorical tent found pitched in my backyard.

Then and only then, I could nod my head in recognition, finally able to name and accept this tent of ambiguous grief. I could close my eyes and take a deep breath. I could let this grief — this overwhelming, all-encompassing sadness called ambiguous loss — have its way with me and in me.

Welcoming it to the neighborhood, I could all at once bid it an eventual farewell.

For this is not forever, but this is for now.

This is *the* now.

[1] Woods, Sarah B. "Covid-19 and Ambiguous Loss." Psychology Today, May 8, 2020: https://www.psychologytoday.com/us/blog/in-sickness-and-in-health/202005/covid-19-and-ambiguous-loss

Hours of Brightness

by Lauren Camp

First published in Under a Warm Green Linden

We woke to the map of England or Paris. Now alert
about Asia, or contemporary versions of the green
of Sweden that made us afraid of the long
side of oceans. We woke and we readied
to wake. The atlas we used to love
for its aggregate had turned to compartments
of danger, not countries, continents,
mountains we'd hope to climb or museums
to study. Every hour, there are people who choose
to crook bridges, concerts and markets
to leave less. Thousands of miles
and miles, and overturned
lives, and this poem is a ruin
of burdens: all those streets, concerts and markets.
I have always been jealous
of people's travels, how they manage to begin
once upon a time with every winter
they spend in Hawaii, each spring in the restful
blue hip of Greece. My husband and I made the bed, pulling taut
our sheets, and the bed was still a meadow,
a market, inviting. Our house in the village
could be described as imperfect, but our house
peddles its pleasures: dust
in the corners and ant workers purging
the cat dish. I have no perception of ideal. Our bed is soft
with small therapies for drifting
or silence, and the huge story
of moon is one of life's repeatable
lessons. It is almost impossible to resist wanting
the conclusion of any journey, craving
one's own framework
for sleeping. But now I'm confessing to a failure
to leaving. Even in my small town,
there are *encounters*. Even in Walmart
one can be hijacked beside the pharmaceuticals.
I've seen it happen. Get up lazybones, my mother said
every morning, as I burrowed my head
deeper, bedecked by the dark
under the blankets. Rise and shine, she'd trill as she swept
through the room. I've never been ready
for a day's most voluptuous edge.
Those hours of brightness have consequence.

Relaxed
by Ryan Buell

I will not admit to knowing where we're headed
just about anyone can see into the future
I feel this most while gazing into insect eyes
disguised as mirror-screens of my own
thoughts programmed backwards
into reptilian rituals meant to calm the mind
almost always leading to increased anxiety
a lens burns through the looker's cranium
ring of crinkled forehead opens like a circle onto red
veins capillaries fade into fragile bone-shield
shattered eggshell pieces in my breakfast
miles and miles deep into sunless starless oceans
rare taste of honeysuckle nectar from light green
stigma the style of stigmata-memories from

Entropy
by Margaret Preigh

One day, they say
the universe will become dark.
All light decayed to ambient energy,
to buzzing heat
spread thin to stillness.
The stars will swallow themselves,
their own glow
and the light of others,
with a hungry gravity.
The boil of fusion
dimmed red,
to a heat contained by numbers that
fit inside a classroom.
The universe is empty,
a cloud of swirling gas and dust
dispersed too far to exist.
Everything that is
and ever was
and ever will be,
drifting away from itself.
Dissociation in distance,
an erasure.

Notes on Blackouts

by Naihobe Gonzalez

Previous version published in The Offing *in March 2020*

Blackout #2

I rush to pick up Tati from preschool, wondering how long this one's going to last and whether the dictator will blame a cable-eating iguana again. We join the people spilling out of shut-down metro stations like ants, paying for the sun's brightness with our sweat. I grip Tati's hand—hopefully not too tight—as we weave in and out of mostly empty stores, looking for precious ice to save the food we have at home from rotting. Only the lucky few with foreign currency on hand can afford that luxury. (We are one of the lucky few—barely.) Finally, I slide my last ten-dollar bill across a counter and get some frozen water in return.

By the time we get home, the power is back. And our microwave is fried.

I stuff the marked-up bag of melting ice inside our freezer and lie down next to Tati while the air conditioning blows on our overheated bodies, offering some artificial comfort.

Blackout #3

Is it still a blackout if light flickers in and out, in and out, in and out, teasing, torturing?

"We have to turn off the breakers!" I call out to my dad. My pocketbook—and psyche—cannot handle any more ruined appliances.

I tell him he should go home before it gets dark, but he insists on staying. It's late Saturday evening, and the sun is still refusing to set. We sit by the open window and eat ham sandwiches that taste of bugspray.

"Why can't I open the fridge, Mami?" Tati asks me.

I explain about perishable food. She listens, and rattles off her favorite foods, asking if they are pah-rah-sha-ble. Chocolate milk? Yes. Chocolate? No—though it will melt in this heat.

When night comes, neighbors start banging pots and cursing the dictator. I want to join their chorus, but I try not to curse around Tati. And anyway, what's the point of yelling his name into the darkness? The hum of his electric generator will drown out our voices. Below, young people dance and drink around a bonfire. A woman's scream in the distance is cut short.

Tati asks what's happening. I hug her close and tell her, and myself, not to worry. It might just be for my benefit, but she nods. Her hair still smells of shampoo: clean, pure. When she gets up to go to the bathroom, I remind her not to flush the toilet.

"Why?" she asks.

"There's no electricity to pump up water all the way up to the 11th floor," I say matter-of-factly. I keep having to teach my daughter unexpected lessons.

Blackout #4

I check my phone every so often, shutting the screen off as quickly as I can. But the phone still dies and I still know nothing. The apartment smells of days' worth of our unflushed piss and shit. No power means no water means no dignity.

My body craves a long shower, but the best I can give it is a washcloth and a bucket. I scrub hard, feeling sorry for myself as I salvage the dirty water that washes off me so I can use it to flush the toilet.

Somehow, that "bath" and that "flush" make me feel better, just a bit, and I finally agree to join Tati in a game of War. But my bad mood has infected her.

"Come on, Tati," I say, holding out the deck of cards. "Let's play."

"I don't want to anymore," she says, hugging her knees into her body.

"You can't just sit there and sulk."

She doesn't flinch, not even to swat away the mosquito circling her head, and I want to join her in sulking. Instead I sit down in front of her and shuffle the deck.

"Pick out a card, any card. Go on—just don't show it to me." Tati looks at me with guarded interest. I keep holding out the deck until she finally bites. "Now memorize the card. You got it?"

She nods timidly, and I ask her to slide the card back in, face down. I squint and make a big show of looking through the deck until the dramatic reveal.

"Is this it?"

Her eyes widen, and she stands up.

"Mami! How'd you do that?"

Despite the dictator's worst attempts, I can still make my daughter believe in magic.

Blackout #5

Tati runs from her room to the kitchen.

"Mami, turn off the breakers!" she yells, her little face scrunched up with adult worry. I hope she doesn't notice what that does to me.

The last blackout—the Big One—lasted four days and even had its own trending hashtag (I later learned). That time the dictator talked of an electromagnetic war waged by Yankee hackers. But not of living in your own stink or throwing away rotted food you'd stood in line for hours to buy. Not of the savage looting and the terror it brought. Not of the people who took water from broken pipes and open sewers and contaminated rivers. Not of the children in hospitals without backup generators who died.

That afternoon, Tati nestles into my armpit and dozes off. Her body feels warm, maybe too warm. I rest the back of my hand on her forehead and lie awake fantasizing about ways the dictator could die. I visualize at least a dozen scenarios: a sniper puncturing his bloated body, a surging mob trampling him …, until the filaments in the lightbulb overhead start glowing again.

"Thank God," I mutter. Gratitude congeals into rage, but I remain still, so as not to rouse Tati. The light wakes her up anyway. I pretend I'm asleep when she gets up to celebrate the good news.

Blackout #6

Tati and I are riding on the elevator when suddenly, the blackness envelops us. It feels like my organs drop first before the rest of my body follows. I pick Tati up and squeeze her to my chest, as if I can absorb the impact of the fall for both of us.

"I'm so sorry," I whisper into her neck, waking up just as we're about to hit the ground.

My eyes are open, but the nightmare is not over—everything is still pitch black. I decide I won't let Tati get on elevators anymore. Or ride the metro. These are a game of Russian roulette now. The bedsheets stick to my body as I try, in vain, to go back to sleep.

Blackout #7

I'm sick in bed with chikungunya, pinned down by pain that seems to be splitting my joints apart. According to the internet, "the disease rarely results in death; those most vulnerable are the elderly, newborns, and young children". That gives me little comfort. Tati is in the living room with my dad. If either of them were to get sick—.

A hot-and-cold despair spreads through my insides. I try to calm myself down by remembering so many others have it worse than us. But it's a dangerous thought—won't there always be someone who's worse off, somehow, somewhere? Am I accepting the unacceptable? Also dangerous: I don't notice the smell from the unflushed toilets much anymore.

Blackout #8

Tati started kindergarten but has only gone to school eight days this month. We are hostages inside our home.

"Why can't we go outside?" Tati whines, her face flushed and shiny.

I look out the window at our once-bustling city that is now stuck in a perpetual state of Sunday. It's only been six months since our microwave died, but we've both aged so much more in that time span.
"It's not safe," I say.

"But why?" And after no answer: "When are things gonna be normal again?"

How do I tell her I have no way of knowing?

10

I remember the night I spent imagining the dictator's death and feel defeated. That's not the kind of person I am.

"Please be quiet," I say, too tired to mother. Maybe it's the lingering fatigue from the chikungunya. I see the hurt in her eyes and I hate myself for it.

Blackout #9

When the water comes back just after midnight, we rush to fill every bottle, bucket, pot, jar, and old Chinese takeout container. This is our new routine. We don't even care that the water is increasingly a murky brown.

Tati waves the mosquitoes away while I work, wanting to help even though she should be asleep for school tomorrow. My dad strains to keep up. I wish I could just work alone, or not at all. But those choices are not available.

The blackouts don't make headlines anymore, but by now I've seen slum kids bathing and playing in sewage waters with my own eyes. I've ridden past them on my way to work, just like I've ridden past dirty children scrounging through trash and begging for food. Long ago, the dictator promised we'd one day be able to swim in the river-turned-sewage-drainage that cuts through our city. Funny how his words came true.

I am thinking of all the children the dictator has hurt while I wait for a bucket to finish filling, when I notice the stream slowing. I twist the handle further, until it won't twist anymore, but that does nothing to the waning water pressure. Just then, Tati runs to hand me a two-liter bottle to fill and trips over the bucket.

All that precious liquid wasted.

"Jesus fucking Christ!" I yell, kicking the empty bucket against the wall. "Why do you have to make everything more difficult?"

My dad helps Tati up. But she's already kneeling back down, using her little hands for the impossible task of saving the water, gulping down her tears like they're made of the chocolate milk I haven't been able to buy her in I don't know how long.

I leave the apartment and wait in the stairwell for my pent-up screams to dissipate inside my throat. If I were to scream aloud, only Tati and my dad would truly hear me—everyone else would just pretend nothing had happened.

I have no idea how much time has passed before I go back in.

Blackout #13

I started keeping these notes so I wouldn't forget. One day we (or someone, if we all die before the darkness ends) will look back at these days and say there were blackouts. We/they will use words like "humanitarian crisis" but we/they won't remember what that truly meant. I know because I already want to forget the details of what we've endured, for my own sanity. But I won't let the dictator get off that easy. I must keep writing.

What's that adage my mom used to say before she died?

There's no evil that lasts a hundred years, nor anybody that can bear it that long.

Blackout #14

It's a storybook kind of Sunday, so I offer to take Tati to the beach. I even convince my dad to go. We carefully make our way down the 11 flights of stairs, three generations.

When I was a kid, I loved that first glimpse of ocean, so blue and expansive. Now I like to see Tati's face taking it in. Nature is still nature, and aside from a trio of emaciated dogs roaming around, the beach is as idyllic as I remember. Tati's eyes brighten with anticipation. I wonder if she'll remember this day when she's my age.

After taking a dip, Tati starts to build a sandcastle. I love how the sand glistens on her skin, how her salt-laced curls spiral, how hard she concentrates on everything she does. She is perfect, my daughter. I must find a way to give her something more than survival.

"Want any help with that castle?" I ask.

She shakes her head, droplets of water dotting the sand around her. "It's not a castle," she says. "It's a new house for us, without stairs."

She turns away from me and gets back to work.

Hair
by Dakota Valdez

i watched it scatter
upon the ground like
uncooked pasta
the color of wise
squid ink
strands hit the floor
each alone in time
and all at once.
a ritual
morphed into change:
you cut the endings,
the weight of loss,
to mourn—
an act of grief
to relieve the living.
----
i cut it all
to welcome peace.

Grover Hot Springs, #33
by Kathryn Jordan

Twenty years of camping on the Eastern Sierra, we climbed
out of the steep box canyon, ascent nearly vertical,
legs leaden, fingers puffed in summer heat. Mountains
beyond mountains recharged my sturdy heart as I plodded,
        determined to keep up with you.

Now we sit on our favorite log, meadow faded in the gloaming,
watching bats hunt. In the west, last vestige of light on the rim
of this vast granite bowl, tall cedars print a row of letters
on the flat page of sky. "Some people think that trees
have feelings," you say. We *muse*: when did sonar first leap
from a bat's head? How did a chloroplast cell grab *radiance*,
excite electrons, jump energy levels, making sugar for earth
to eat? I sense you beside me in the dark, sure and comforting
        as vanilla scent of Jeffrey Pines.

It's been a rough year, my son, and yet we're here once again,
safe under the vault of heaven, stars just clearing space to shine.
It was never a given I'd make it up that ridge, that I'd reach
the tree line, hauling old bones after you to bare tundra, my feet
trudging behind yours, maintaining enough space between us
        for talc-like dust to settle.

The Disposable Mask is the New Plastic Bag
by Tina Cane

like the broken wing of a blue jay   the color of a robin's egg   and today

my youngest son   wept his body limp   with the million things   he's seen and heard

in his ten years   these past few months   his sister assures me   he understands

everything   just doesn't have the words   but I am not assured   I can feel all

the languages   pulsing at his temple   beneath my lips   I kiss his hot skin

press my cheek   too hard against his   trying to absorb   every bit of hurt from him

to take on his sadness   and mask my own   having mistook   a swatch of fabric

for a swath of sky   so eager to find a sign   of the advent of spring

and shepherd him back   to simpler things

Victory Garden
by Edith Friedman

In the spring of our immurement
while floating spores danced along our paper borders
gold ingots failed and fear maps metastasized
we built a vegetable box.
Stone walls four feet thick, a steel-runged ladder
tomato cages taller than watchtowers.
Ten cubic yards of compost
(dray horse, water ox, hundred-mile gull)
clogged our nostrils. We planted
thick-skinned eggplants, peppers hot as boiling oil,
mouth-sting mustard greens.
Between the rows, we sowed blood dandelions –
leather rootstalks store for months
in the lead-lined cellar by the backyard well.
Nail shut the mailbox. Let summer come.

Picas
by Klein Vorhees

The swamp unearths
another newborn
rising up from its drowning,
cries crawling to the shore
with no priest to translate
sob to song.

Every stick breaks
in my hands
when I try to weave a basket
to carry my sins like keepsakes—

a velvet bow barrette (burgundy)
a string of skeleton keys (all but one rusted)
a sick boy's cough (kissed.)

I bury my hands
beneath the mudbank,
scoop out the psalms and swallow
silted song, building up
in my throat
until I can do nothing
but sing.

I have a hard question,
would Grandma have loved
who I am

14

a cloud shifting overhead.

When you die
God lets you choose
one omen
to send back to earth.

On her deathbed,
my grandmother
said she would send
cardinals to us.

That's the easiest question
you've ever asked me.

It's Here at Your Familiar Street-Corner
by Rusty Morrison

It's here at your familiar   street-corner in the morning's
rushed traffic, you realize   a woman is in you. She
has maybe always been here   staring, through your eyes, outward
at others. Her eyes are bees   foraging out from a hive
they've spent years making without   their letting you taste more than
bee-sting. You've grown the busy   colony of her, within
the wild occluded landscape   unnervingly most present
in your dreams. Or has it been   she, who has cultivated
you as an outward cell that   protects the grub-like larvae
within. Or do you use now   the otherness of bees to
ignore what you will only   let yourself see as the life
of grubs still-born within you,   the life you've never become?

Mint

by Christine Hyung-Oak Lee
Previously published in The Rumpus

Mint is a perennial, sprouting up year after year, and the plant is hard to kill.
Mint loves water, but it can survive a drought. Mint loves light, but it can survive
the darkness. Mint prefers well-drained soil, but it can survive in clay. I once left
a pot of mint unattended while I was on vacation; a month later, the terracotta
planter held a brown plant cadaver. But then it rained. The next day, the carcass
sprouted a leaf.

Mint is invasive. You must plant it within a container to control its domain.
However, its stolons can still jump a pot and once in the open soil, it thrives and
spreads with aggressive vigor and chokes the life out of other plants. Mint is
unstoppable.

Mint transforms others within proximity. If you plant mint straight into the
ground, you must keep it separate from other herbs. It will make its surrounding
neighbors taste like mint, too.

Mint is the smell of the oil my yoga teacher rubs on my temples as I collapse in
corpse pose at the end of class. Anointed, I lay breathing and emulating the dead,
try to approach the brink of a dark sleep. I attempt to wipe my mind clean, but
the mint invades all thoughts, keeps me awake. The mint smells like rape.

Each morning, I brush my teeth with mint toothpaste. For years, I didn't know
why the taste bothered me. Only that it did. It made me tense. The toothbrush in
my mouth, forcing the mint upon my tongue, nauseated me, made me gag. But I
had to brush my teeth, so I endured. In those days, mint flavored toothpaste was
all there was.

When there is a sprig of mint in my lemonade, I pick it out.

I was at my friend's birthday party last spring. His black and white dog likes to
lie in the green mint patch, the stems standing up around him like miniature pine
trees. The dog rolls, and as we sip wine, we smell the crushed mint. When the
dog springs up, so does the crushed mint.

Would you like a mint, he asks. He leans in, the smell of hot mint and steak dinner gusting out of his mouth. No thank you, I say. No thank you.

Mint is often used in aromatherapy. Ingested, it helps digestion. It is an anti-
septic. It relieves sore throats. When I am sick with a sore throat, I buy cherry
lozenges. They say mint is soothing for the throat. But it is not soothing for mine.

It relieves stress. It feels cool, but it can also burn. Mint is deceptive.

I put mint in my baby's food, pureed peaches with flecks of mint. I don't want
her to be afraid of mint. I want to expand her palate. I want her to be resilient like
mint.

He was popular. A ladies man. He introduced me to so much. To too much. I was twenty years old. We went to bars—he charmed the doormen at exclusive clubs into letting me enter. Even charmed old Bruno at the Persian Aub Zam Zam into making me a drink, a gin martini—the only kind he made, without ID. Bruno leaned into him and said loud enough so I could hear, "You're lucky she looks so young."

The peppermint soap, the only soap he has in his shower, burns my crotch, the part of my body that splits in two, as I wash him off of me. From inside of me. I know that the parts that burn, are the parts that bleed, the parts that were touched and torn.

There are only a few ways to kill mint. Rust, for one, can kill mint. But aside from chemical weed killers, you can douse it with a concoction of salt, soap, and vinegar. Or you can pour boiled water over it. But you must do this over and over again. To kill its leaves, and stems, and its rhizomes, which when you dig them up, are a thick mat of knots. There is so much beneath the soil.

I can never forget. I cannot forget the night I drink five single malt scotches with five beer backs, and we fall into a tangled mess onto the bed, like in a movie. A movie has actors, people who play characters other than themselves. And that night, we are ourselves but something shifts, we are becoming something other than ourselves. He has become something monstrous, a machine that will not stop. He gropes me and rapes me. With force, without humanity, with effort, without compassion, relentless. The pain turns the night into a white light, and I say no. We have never had sex this way before. No. I whisper it. I hiss it. I plead it. I scream. No. No. No. He says it will be over soon. To stay still. But it is not over. I say No. No. No. And it is never ever over after that.

And then I am no longer in the bed. I am no longer the person being raped. I am on the ceiling looking down. That night I become an actress. I am in the corner looking away. I am the air in the room. I am the mint in the planter in the corner of the room. I am holding my breath. I do not need to breathe. I am numb. I am the girl I was in high school who cut herself to feel, even if the thing I felt was pain. Because she was numb in every other way. Because I had locked up every feeling, because I was taught that vulnerability and sadness and helplessness were unacceptable and I would catch those feelings in a net every night and tamp them down, so that I became the expert fisherman of my emotions. But like mint, they never died.

Mint can become leggy and unattractive. The more you cut your mint, the thicker it will become.

He offers me a cup of peppermint tea, green leaves floating in hot water in the morning, after I have showered so that my privates feel singed with mint. "I'm sorry," he says, "I don't know what came over me last night." He says it with tenderness absent the night before.
I say nothing. I stare at him. Wonder who he is. Who he was. Wonder what happened. Confused. I am still numb. I am parched. I am in the dark. My feet feel stuck in clay. I don't say anything. I don't say anything as he drives me back over

the Bay Bridge to my dorm room. The morning fog is cold and fresh and stings my face, not unlike mint, as I hold on to his leather jacket on the motorcycle.

When we break up, because we don't break up right away, because I can't believe what has happened, that I said no, and he still kept going, because he was my boyfriend, because I felt I was a willing participant, because I had yet to learn to stand up for myself, yet to become angry, he says we should try to be friends. That maybe we could keep seeing each other while seeing other people, to ease the transition. And then I finally have the words. I tell him I don't want to be friends. That he can have me or not at all. That he had me, and now he cannot.

Twenty years later, he still calls me. He says, "I have been diagnosed with mania."

A light shines down on that dark room twenty years ago. "That makes sense," I say.

"It does?"

"It makes sense." I try hard not to hang up. "It explains what happened that night."

"What night?"

"The night after which you said, 'I'm sorry, I don't know what came over me.'"

"Oh, that night." He sighs. "Yeah. Probably."

"Well," I say, "thanks for the closure. It helps." And I hang up.

I tell my husband the man called. I light up a menthol cigarette.

"Honey," he says over the phone, "He raped you because he wanted to rape you."

I want to forget.

"Honey," he continues. "There is no excuse."

"And you cheated on me because you wanted to cheat on me."

My husband pauses. "If you want to lump me with him, yes."

I want to forget.

Out of my mouth, a cloud of mint smoke.

Thought Log #4
by Maw Shein Win

Wind rattling glass doors.
Feldenkrais decreases reactivity.
Trumpet vine, Winter creeper, ivy.
Build in microbreaks.
I said figs not dates.
Alternate between high and low impact activities.
Palm trees have feelings, too.
My mother had a blood clot in her brain.
I ace the mountain pose.
Modern science does not support the classical elements of the material basis
for the physical world.
Chin, shawl, nut.
The year my identity was stolen.
I consider luck to be a viable option.
Glass of apple wine disappears and reappears from green screen.
Smoke trails above trails.
Emerald swans.

White Bird
by Matthew Brailas

It takes up behind his house in early spring.
He calls it the ibis
because of its curved beak,

antenna legs,
because the name is pretty.
In the evenings, if the bugs aren't bad,

he props his feet and watches it
preening at the water's edge.
When the sun is right,

its feathers scatter the rays
and the ibis becomes a shimmering pane
so bright it hurts to look at.

But he is still coming out of winter.
You can see under his skin
blue lines and the capillaries

around his eyes
and he thinks it is obscene
to reject all that light.

You Ask
by Jules Henderson

You ask
and I say *delicious*
(that cell/splitting glory that
unfolds until we expire)
        angels on fire
                come remind us
that this life
is just a prayer

we have been
rendezvousing with the dead
in the small hours
        they say death is nothing
                but a change of clothes
and setting the stage before
the next act

we are corpsing
our way
through a comedy hour
        so as not to let on
                that we are amused
so as not to expose ourselves
as alive

while they climb Jacob's ladder
we drive along the coast and
make waves with
        one hand out the window
                pushing through air with an open palm
and it is our prayer
(all this living
is just a prayer)

notes, after maggie nelson & darcie wilder
by Lily Darling

1.   every morning my grandmother gathers a flower for her dead.

2.   "it starts the day off okay," she tells my dad, because she only ever really addresses my dad, especially now. probably something to do with me looking like my mother, or purely for the fact that i am a daughter. i am too tired most days to navigate the implications of either

3.   "it starts the day off okay," she tells my dad. "it's a hard time"

4.   it is january and christmas is over and it is only me and my dad and my grandma in her little boca living room. she's wringing her hands like she always does, and she's the one who starts because she's been "just waiting for this christmas to finally be over" because "once i got through this first thanksgiving and then christmas--" the unspoken words "without you" hover over us--"i thought it could finally be over. now i just have to make it through may first"

5.   she is wringing her hands like she always does in photographs, some thing i only noticed once you pointed it out. she is wringing her hands and telling us about the light in her reading room that once turned on in the middle of the night, that she thinks this was you. you in a gentle visitation. you in a bright bulb, a brilliant white light

6.   earlier, in the car, my dad tells me that you would have hated how sentimental we were being about all of this and yea, he's probably right isn't he

7.   your sister, my other aunt, tells me she has a dream where she is mopping up your weeping. austin told me at the wake that his dreams are so vivid it feels like he just doesn't sleep anymore. it makes me want to wrap him in my arms and never let go because it's hard enough to be thirteen and trans in texas and it's hard enough to be thirteen and trans and it's hard enough to be thirteen without his mother and it's hard enough

8.   in the only dream i've had about you, you found me in a crowd as i was searching for an old lover. you grabbed my face and pressed your fore head to mine and said "we are in this together" and then you were gone. i'd like to say that i woke up then, that that was all there was, but i kept looking for him, even after that. i'm sorry

9.   do we practice mourning for ourselves or for the person who is lost

10.   in houston, they opened your computer and the first thing she saw in the search bar was "how to tell your kids you're going to die from cancer"

11.   woolf once said something like we learn through our mothers and does that mean trauma too

12.   sometimes harper will post her saved videos of you to her snapchat on the anniversaries of their taking, i sometimes open my bleary eyes in the morning only to see them, unexpected: you dancing with her in your car, your smile, your laugh, your love

13.   i learned you died through her instagram post. that's fucked up

14.   my mom told me she and my dad wanted me to "have the day" so they didn't tell me until noon. it was finals week and they had taken you off

life support that morning and all i remember is sitting in front of the library

15.   i wouldn't describe it as crying maybe more like making sound

16.   lisa came outside and held me and walked me back to my dorm and we lay in my bed for i don't remember how long

17.   the first time i did coke i made all my friends omelets even though i have never successfully made an omelet in my life. they came out perfectly. you weren't dead yet and if you were i think you would have known so i wish i could have told you because you would have loved that

18.   my first eating disorder therapist tells me i talk about men and hot cheetos in the same way

19.   i would do anything to see you laugh again

20.   over dinner my friend says we never talk about mommy issues because it doesn't turn into a fetish just bad poetry

21.   okay so remember that time in houston where we sat on your couch and you talked about the last time you were hospitalized & how they accidentally overdosed you on morphine & how my dad almost watched you die right in front of him yea right there slowly over the course of hours & the doctors were gone for the weekend so no one knew what was going on even though the iv bag with the broken stopper was *right there right above both of your heads* & you talked about how you hallucinated that there was this skinny black figure curled at the end of your bed & it just sat there watching you & scratching your legs & then it was under your bed pawing at the mattress under you & you could *feel* it it was *right there* & that story makes me so scared because you genuinely were dying then & is that what it's gonna be is that all there is is that it

22.   okay like for the three months after max and i broke up the groupchat on instagram with him me daniel alex was still active & i remember one morning i had just woken up from another dream where max was raping me again but it was right after it happened when i went into the bathroom & just listened to the sound of my own breathing & in the dream his mom kept knocking on the door & i was crying so hard i woke myself up & i opened my phone & there was the notification from the groupchat & one of them had sent a video with no message attached & so i opened it &it was a guy jumping off a fucking building & he hit the ground &pinkmist &i had the heaviest feeling in my throat but i never left the groupchat because they would have made fun of me like that matters & daniel said something like bro that's fucked but it didn't sound like he meant it it sounded like he was laughing & he probably was

23. yeah, alright, so okay in march i ate molly & when i purged the next morning it was all blood thick&blackredorange in the porcelain curve of the toilet i am glad you weren't dead then yet or else you might have seen that happen that would have been embarrassing

24. he said he didn't hear me begging him to stop & that's why he didn't

25. & in the video there was a crowd of people filming as it happened & the police were trying to keep them back but weren't doing anything about the filming & why were they doing that what could they be doing with that video still on their phone why

26. sometimes it feels like i just blink okay and now i'm in your car & that means this was your car & that means you were was once here & now you aren't anymore but it's still your car, you know, the one my dad refuses to go into the one he had a breakdown in on the louisiana interstate, that long overdue homecoming through my great-grandmother's old town & witnessing a rainbow that could have been her or you welcoming him back & bad songs on the radio & good barbecue in his stomach & he did it all in your car, which means he was transporting all the leftover pieces, harper included, in the passenger seat with her dirty airforce 1s & now i am the one in your car, with harper, who is wearing the same airforce 1s & playing the same music my dad hated but i can't help love for how incessantly hopeful it is & i look over my right shoulder & try to ignore how uncomfortable i am with my legs all twisted to accommodate both our purses & harper is driving with the ease of a woman her mother will never see her become & harper is wearing a scarf around her head with her sunglasses low low on her nose like all the models she adores & she's telling me about her new boyfriend & looking back there is only the big dumb slate of the interstate & a cvs & a homeless man with a bad leg & big bright blue skies & lots of palm trees & i ask harper where she got her sunglasses & she says "i think they're my mom's" & we both go quiet

27. my dad shuts down for a second every time your name appears in conversation, i can see it happen in his eyes

28. sometimes deaths cut clean--not immediately, but after a while things get more quiet. maybe it's sad to say but it's true you know

29. yours didn't

30. over dinner, at our little table for two, my dad tells me that it has only gotten worse as time has gone on. he tells me this every time i come home, now, as if it is the first time he is telling me. every time he does i nod, reach my hand out to clasp his. note the heavy amnesia paired with grief

31. my dad will still wake up crying sometimes. i think you know that. i think you would want him to start healing by now. i do too

32.   okay so in my grandma's living room we rehearse our visitation stories. it's January and Christmas is over and she has just finished crying into her hands as my dad and i sit on either side of her and i open my mouth

33.   my visitation story, the one i rehearse gently to my audience of him and her and maybe you, too, as i make eye contact with only the floor:

34.   okay alright so, i was in my dorm, maybe three days after they took you off life support, sitting on my floor and staring at a book of poetry. i was listening to one of my dad's old records, not for the melodrama of it but because it reminds me of my childhood home and him and you and your little feet propped up on the dashboard of his car as he drove you to school every day and so of course i was listening to this record and pretending to read those words on that page and so

35.   okay so, i was in my dorm, pretending like a book of poems can be something i could press myself into for at least a little bit and become something new. something stronger

36.   and when rodger waters got to that part, that part you know, yea, the "heaven from hell/blue skies from" but he never finished it because at that moment the record player's needle lifted, because it lifted and scratched over the face of the vinyl in one extended, warbling note. as if someone had pushed it. as if someone refused to let him finish his sen tence.

37.   as if you were there.

I Can(not) Hear the Bells
by Sam Weiland

Sofia's voice rang out from my phone resting on my desk. "Meghan just had her baby a few months ago! She was pregnant at the wedding but didn't tell anybody apparently and then yeah, she had her baby in February!"

I was sitting at my desk, in the middle of eating a last minute dinner I realized I needed to eat, when she called to catch up. I had settled on one of my specialties, a fan favorite I had developed over the years— a thrown together with whatever-I-could-find-in-the-fridge microwave quesadilla. I know this is disrespectful to quesadillas but a girl's gotta eat. Sofia and I had texted earlier in the week about finding a time to chat, and I had nearly forgotten until I saw her name and a photo of us in tiny red cap and gowns at our kindergarten graduation fill my screen.

"Wait… what! You're kidding, she was pregnant? At the wedding?" I could hardly believe it. Not just that Meghan had been pregnant and already had the kid, but that Sofia was thrilled for her. I set down the slice of quesadilla I had been nibbling on, eyeing it with suspicion. As if it might betray me and announce itself, letting Sofia know that my idea of being a functioning adult was not Midwestern marriage, 2.5 babies and Craftsman style houses. I was the version

24

of adult who buys organic wine purely because it's on sale, who revels in being able to live alone, and who microwaves tortillas and cheese for dinner because she lost track of time, noticed the sun had gone down, and hadn't eaten since breakfast.

"Yeah, I know right! That's why she wasn't drinking!" she said. I could hear her beaming through the phone. She sounded so genuinely happy for her friend, as if it was the most normal thing in the world for Meghan to do. To have a baby, to become a mom, to suddenly be wholly responsible for another human. Somehow Sofia had passed through the doorway that leads to the time in our lives when everyone is getting married and having kids and it's acceptable, expected even. I still stood not just outside that door, but at a safe, unthreatening distance away from it so as to avoid any potential side effects of getting too close—including but not limited to self-doubt, jealousy, inadequacy, or worse, "baby fever."

"Oh my, wow…" I struggled to find the right words, ones that attempted to match Sofia's own excitement while also not revealing how much I could not relate to wanting to be married and have kids so young. "I can't believe she was pregnant at your wedding and no one knew! And that she already had the baby! She must've been fairly far along then…? Or wait, no—I guess yours and Aaron's wedding was a while ago now, wasn't it? Huh… If that was in June and then she gave birth in February… She would've been what? A few months? Or wait… no—less than that? Ah! Math! I mean it doesn't matter! Either way, that is so so… wild! Wow, I just can't believe it! But Meghan definitely seemed like she would be a great mom…"

I rambled. Tried to bring it back at the end, but I knew I wasn't going to win any Academy Awards for that performance. I bit the nail on my thumb ever so slightly, worried I'd have to explain that it wasn't that I didn't understand why they wanted to get married and give up their independence and settle down and stop making decisions purely for themselves and have kids, just—what was the rush?

"Yeah, totally. It's funny, too, because her dad used to say that he knew his whole life that he wanted to be a dad. Just like… a great dad. And he was—is one. And Meghan was that way too—she always knew she wanted to be a mom, like since she was a kid. Now she is one! I'm just so happy for her."

"Oh wow, yeah that *is* funny… and that's so exciting for her and her husband!" I really was trying to convey some sort of agreement surrounding the excitement and happiness they all must be feeling.

"I know! When I was talking about it with my mom she asked how long the baby was, it was such a typical thing for my mom to ask. Because Meghan and Tate are so tall, my mom was like, 'That baby probably has such long limbs!' Too funny. But oh my gosh, Sammy, whenever you have a baby, I bet that its legs are going to be sooo long too!"

My uterus recoiled at the mention of having to house a fetus for nine months. My legs tightened. I was grateful we were having this conversation over the phone so

Sofia couldn't see the complete and utter panic etched across my face. I gripped the ridges of my hips, my fingers pushing into my pelvis and my thumbs jamming into the excess fat and skin on my lower back. I glanced down at my stomach, at the layer of fat that I learned in a physiology class had a specific purpose for women, which was why it seemed no amount of crunches or sit ups or twists or plank minutes could get rid of it. This particular layer of fat on my body, the one I affectionately called my couch pouch, was supposed to *protect* my reproductive organs— as a woman, according to this professor, I was biologically predetermined by evolution to participate in the old fashioned miracle of childbearing. *'When' I have a baby?! No thank you!*

"Oh geez," I forced a laugh, "Well we'll definitely have to see about that." I chuckled again for emphasis. She laughed too and I wondered for another second if she could see through me, hear the counterfeit in my voice, but she didn't acknowledge it.

"So yeah, and Raina's wedding is in June so hopefully we'll all get to see the baby then," Sofia continued with the same nonchalance in all of her announcements regarding engagements and weddings and babies.

"Wait, what!" I felt like a broken record, "Raina! She got engaged?"

"Oh wait— I didn't tell you? Yeah! Raina got engaged maybe... a month? After our wedding."

I was silently trying to do more mental math. Trying to figure out the algorithms, timelines, diagrams and graphs that might add up or help me understand how these massive life events were unfolding at rapid pace right in front of me.

It hadn't even been a year since Sofia had gotten married. Less than a year since I shut a part of my conscience off, went against all of my morals and flew to a wedding in Iowa in the peak of a global pandemic. Flew to be in the wedding of one of my closest friends since we were five years old. To be there to show my support and my love for my friend. That painfully long weekend in Iowa, I had met Meghan and Raina and everyone from the second part of Sofia's life, the people she had found at her conservative college in Minnesota. Meghan had been married just over a year to her husband, Tate, and I found we didn't have much to chat about other than she had been an English major too and was currently tutoring high school students part time for the SATs. Raina, the maid of honor, was Sofia's best friend from college, the person she apparently experienced a religious reawakening in Austria with, and the youngest of four girls. Both of Raina's older sisters were already married, which made Raina an expert on all things wedding, bachelorette and bridal. It also seemed to cause Raina to clarify every time her sisters were mentioned that they were married while she still was not. But she had been dating a guy, a red headed man named Adam or Ryan or Blake, for awhile now and she thought they were on the right track. A guy she had just been friends with in undergrad and even though she didn't really find him that attractive back then, she assured me she had seen him in a new light when he slid into her DMs a few months ago.

26

"Stop, oh my god," more scratches on the record, more repeating myself over and over, "So she's engaged to who... that red headed guy? What was his name? Adam? I thought they had just started dating!"

"Close, Dylan. But yeah, no, they're wedding is in June this summer so me and Aaron will head out to Minnesota for it for a bit and then I think to Iowa to see his family. But we have to plan a trip for me to come visit you!"

"Yes, anytime! Of course! We'll both be vaccinated by then and hopefully things will be somewhat on their way back to normal and I can come visit you guys too. I am dying to see your guys' new place."

Our conversation trailed on back toward familiar spaces of sharing stories about what was going on at work and with school, what books we had been reading lately and how our families were doing. After about an hour of the standard check in, Sofia said she had to run and I had to get back to my cold quesadilla, even though I wasn't all that hungry anymore.

I sat back in my chair, resting my head back and felt a weight crush down against my chest. Not even a year had gone by since I last saw my friend and yet it seemed as if decades worth of life events had been bursting around her nonstop. *Is that how time moves when you go through that doorway to marriage and babies?* Sometimes it seemed as though I could stretch out a moment like taffy, filling it with endless tiny details and tasks and still have room to feel the bittersweet sensation of boredom. I could spend hours in silence, only exchanging a few knowing glances with my dog and not noticing how quiet it had been until my phone rang. Time felt limitless. Forgiving. Malleable. Even when I wanted it to speed up, it never seemed to end. When Sofia itemized her friends' engagements, weddings, childbirths, it was as if their lives were moving at hyper speed. I felt so far behind, so disconnected from that mindset, so very much left in the dust of the slow lane. But I liked it there. I could drive at my pace, I could look around. I could enjoy the view.

Finding Grays
by Krista Varela Posell

As I approach my thirties, I begin obsessing about finding my first gray hair. Whenever I pass a mirror, I can't help but turn my gaze—not to look for stains on my clothes or spinach in my teeth, but to watch out for that first ashen follicle sticking out of my head.
My hair has grown lighter with age, transforming from solid chocolate to various tones of amber, but I have yet to sprout an actual gray. Fairer streaks catch my eye in my reflection and prompt me to go in for a closer look. I spread my hair apart to examine the roots, as if I'm hunting for lice.
I check excessively the way I used to check my underwear every time I went to the bathroom as a preteen, looking for signs of my first menstruation. But it's true when they say a watched pot never boils. My first period arrived on a hot, unexpected spring afternoon when I was eleven, distracted by the men in my

life: my father, who had recently moved out of the house, and a boy, who had given me a tiny silver heart-shaped locket. A locket so tiny that no photo would actually fit inside, but I kept the necklace for years after that boy broke my heart, finding faith for future love in its smallness.

*

Several of my friends have already gotten their first grays, some many times over, their heads beautiful rustic blends of chestnuts, honeys, auburns, and alabasters. My husband included, his temples perfectly salt-and-peppered amongst his curly Jewish locks.

My mother earned her grays in her mid-thirties, just after giving birth to my younger brother; being hospitalized at five months pregnant, having an emergency C-section at seven months, and then bringing home a collicky baby after a month in the NICU undoubtedly sped up her body's internal clock.

So perhaps I still have a few years to go if genes are any indication of this next life phase. But one existential crisis after another begins to fray the ends of my telomeres, as my worlds big and small lack immunity to time and change. As I round the corner on my third decade, I've watched the Amazon, Australia, and my own California backyard go up in flames. I've also witnessed my mother disappear due to early onset dementia, unrecognizable from the woman who shepherded me through that first period and first heartbreak, her own hair now thin and mousey.

I wonder about the vanity behind this obsession of finding gray hairs, whether I'm consumed with this certainty out of excitement or out of dread. Will I embrace those strands when they come like a badge of honor, or will I choose denial and start dying my hair?

*

Five months before my thirtieth birthday, COVID-19 keeps everyone from going to the hair salon and many of us go gray without choice.

Life itself begins to take on a certain grayness, a monochromatism that reflects the sameness of everyday spent inside. I realize that nearly every piece of furniture I own is black—how had I never noticed before?

The Bay Area is unusually cold for weeks: steel clouds loom heavy when I sit on my back deck trying to get some vitamin D, and late spring rains tinge everything with sadness.

I stop checking the mirror obsessively. While the virus ransacks every corner of the world, I stop doing many of the things I used to do. My hair now reaches down to the small of my back and I stop washing it but once a week—I watch it come alive and thicken as the days go on, as if it knows it is capable of its own wildness. I stop shaving: dark hair covers my legs, my underarms, my pubic area, and I observe in awe as my body returns to its own natural order.

*

A short-lived experiment—by the time my birthday rolls around in August, I am desperate for a return to normalcy. I start shaving again even though there is nowhere to go. My hair is still long and untamed, but I no longer search for grays; I've surrendered to accepting their eventual arrival. Instead I focus on bringing more color into my days: curling up with a purple blanket for a nap, placing sage and burgundy succulents on my desk, watching the blue jay that waits in my backyard every morning for my dog to come out and play. I lock away these tiny mementos inside my chest, remembering the hope that comes from preserving what can't be easily bound.

a conversation between the sword and the neck

in memory of Serhenk Yaşar

by Pinar Banu Yasar

who	arms me,
who	weary in yesterday's
	never the backtrack//generation beats back
	with its sentimental molecules//,
who	has the feeling i shed to make neglect
	a poppy-pillowed room,
	keep on taking keep smoke in the shaking
	hand i raise to call you
father	
	while i look away,
Father	
	while wounds grow in the ground
	outside my grandfather's house, pond scum,
	mandoline-fun the soldiers chopping up children,
	Kurdish in the minefield Kurdish in missing sun,
	throwing rocks out to see//to sea//to wreck a land
	with only blood records of its seedlings;
	funeral each afternoon,
	each fig supple moon hued from the aftermath,
	never cried like that before i knew the truth
	never crawled through limbed hell for you
Father,	
	while wombs remain
	the only entrance to the mountains
	where we
	prepare our children
	to lose their arms one day

Kintsugi (a prayer)

The Japanese art of repairing broken pottery with gold or silver lacquer.
by Mary Cisper

Given what's here—a blighted door; a bullet-riddled fender; a cleaved boulder, lichen-covered—you decide to make a film. Flashback: three horses in a corral. An ashy documentary feeling because first horse keeps turning in a circle as the stream erupts silently in bitter cress. It's probably not a fender, it might be a folded-in barrel, rusting. A bullet hole looks like a child's drawing of a star. Then a knot in the plank a branch passed through when the door was alive. The boulder has been there for a few thousand years, the cleft somewhat less. Not that the slope isn't steep or wooded—remember your niece's infant son. (Footage shudders brokenly.) A random pile of sticks may not be man-made. Sometimes a canyon wren sings in the canyon. Second horse stands silent as a nest. Forager, the hammer is wrapped in cloth. So you rise and draw your hand across a branch of what you thought was piñon. A silver thread flows out ahead of you. Who will say a needle is not fur? Forager, if third horse shimmers—

Published in *Glint*, Issue 11, Winter 2020 (online).

Public

Zoom Funeral
By AJ Strosahl

We are shocked when Esther dies on a Monday. We don't think she seems like the type. We remember her 70th birthday a few years ago, when she rented a cedar lodge in the hills and threw a dance party. We remember how fast and how far she could walk. We remember how she made short work of almost everything. We realize, after a while, that dying is no different.

We send cards and flowers to her wife, to her kids. We send soft toys to her grandchildren. We call or write. We tell our spouses and friends and children that we have lost someone and that it is hard. We receive the invitation in our email boxes and we RSVP that yes, we will attend or no, we must sadly decline.   We think the memorial is too soon or not soon enough.

We can do anything on the internet, and will. We are grieving in 164 messy, discrete rooms. We are holding all the funerals in the world at once. We are fighting against our neutral, expectant Zoom meeting expressions. We are keeping our faces grave to make our suffering legible. We are trying not to look at our own reflections. We are cowards with our cameras off. We are names written in a font we can't quite place, against a square black backdrop. We are nodding slowly. We are wearing sweatpants and a nice top. We are recognizing the songs they play and trying not to remember our own associations with them. We are trying to be here, to live in this moment exactly.

We are trying not to laugh at the sheer number of elderly white lesbian Buddhists present because we know Esther would have wanted us to at least try. We are receiving private messages from a guy our college roommate fucked fifteen years ago and two states away, who suddenly appears at this wake, incongruently, and would like to catch up sometime soon. We are calling in from Hawaii, from South Korea, from the Castro, from West Oakland, from Oaxaca, from our living room, from the study where the internet is good, from a bedroom closet where we can be away from the kids.

We are in a soupy, deadened silence, as Esther's godson slowly explains Zoom etiquette to us. We are a blinking grid of muted mics. We are mourners endlessly waiting for our subject to arrive. We are dignified and sorrowful in sol- idarity with the devastated wife. We are sobbing as the physicist son reads that Aaron Freeman piece about the deathlessness of energy. We are patient with the meandering stories told by the brother no one has met before. We are undone as the obstetrician daughter wails that she thought they would have more time. We are wondering what the Zoom equivalent of a funeral crier is. We are wondering what it would be like if someone started rending their clothes or beating their breast. We are remembering other funerals where Mary Oliver poems were read. We are thinking that on balance this one is worse, or is better.

We are bracing ourselves for the open mic portion of the memorial. We are remembering times this has gone wrong in funerals past. We are worried what people might say or are gathering our own thoughts or are trying to decide if there is basis enough for us to speak. We are thinking of how we saw Esther at our Zoom book club the Friday before that Monday she died and she seemed like she was getting better, maybe. We are thinking about the time she came over last year that we didn't know was the last. We are thinking about all the times before she got sick when we were irritated by her dietary restrictions. We are thinking about the times we let her down. We are thinking about how, the last time the cancer came, she beat it back definitively. We are thinking about how she shaved just the sides of her head during chemo and looked so, so cool. We are thinking about how we haven't seen her in over fifty years or how we exchanged emails with her every week or how we were there, in the room, when she died. We are thinking that seven weeks between diagnosis and death is almost no time at all or that it is more time than we had with someone else we loved, who is now gone.

We are speaking now. We are talking about how she came to our house the day our dad died. We are talking about how she was there when our children were born. We are calling her a towering woman. We are telling everyone that we made art with her every Wednesday in our printmaking studio, for eighteen years. We are telling the story of our daughter's wedding, when Esther mended a burst seam in our dress with a sewing kit she had in her purse, saving the day. We are remembering the time we saw her build a platform frame for our boyfriend's futon, with a spare hour and some scavenged two-by-fours. We are desperately wanting to recommend a book we just read, to her and only her. We are seized with wild, entropic grief. We are telling a story of Esther as a child, trying to catch a greased pig at a rodeo, grinning as it shot through her hands.

We are bodiless voices that dissolve into the air.

We are missing her still.

We are flagging.

We are turning off our cameras. We are going to the kitchen to make ourselves a snack. We are typing our remembrance of the entire sum of Esther's life into the chat window. We are reminding her wife to download the chat transcript so she can read it later. We are saying that this was lovely, given the circumstances. We are saying it was nice to see you all here today, kind of. We are remembering our to-do list. We are remembering the work of the day. We are hearing the kids call from the next room or reminding ourselves to check the porch for a package or jumping on our next Zoom call.

We are wiping away our tears.

We are clicking on the rectangular red button.

We are leaving the meeting.

America, Sing Some Awareness

by Sheila Davies Summer

1.
In the entry of America,
at that dark hour,
there were pieces
shined and sharpened
to gather; to steal
and steady against
an enemy, a foe,
opposers foreseen.

2.
The foul spirit
settled. The godawful
hurled a heartless
fate at our faces.
The heathen king
and capitalists,
common and global,
seethed when we persisted.

3.
The hoary and young
thugs, hooded
and bald, were bladed
by verve. The demon,
its fiendish character
ordained the day
by gut, girt, and bowel,
binding fears in mortals,
fumed when we didn't quit.

4.
And we look up,
articulate: it takes the heart
a hard long time to break
convention with surrender and
mend our arms for struggle.
Controlled withholding
of the truth offends.

5.
They chewed all night
to digest America,
the foam of charged particles
traveling at life speed.
Numbers of dead tolled on
our souls, A frontline worker
blasted the meter of his death
sentence with a leaf blower.

6.   America doubles over.
      Everything hurts.
      Takes the knee.
      In the streets. At the test site,
      the clinics, the fields of ICU
      tents, the storage of morgues.
      One creator takes the knee.
      Withheld breaths deliver death.
      The black and the masked
      stumble toward a second
      transfiguration. Memory
      threads the needle
      with a fresh molecular set
      of emotions.

7.   We howl over spilt evolution,
      circled by a cloud of bats.
      When we lose the fire
      of the future, a cold mortal
      northern roars at our backs.
      We attend the dawn of the sky,
      hand-stamped by seven levels
      of atmospheric political conditions.
      We catch your breath, we fold it
      neatly in a cloakroom of air.

8.   I was standing there trying to
      develop love inside an indigo dress
      in the gloaming, in the glower
      of a nonbird-struck bush
      with dark purple fruits among
      dusts of bloomy paraffin
      remastering the tournament
      of the sorrows. "Great Stars"
      I cried under feminine violins.

at the local chain coffee shop over decaf, too late in the day for another expresso
by Stella Santamaria

meeting with very important people, v i p
in a chain coffee shop

thrown into the canon
of profit

canon of self doubt
the canon of self importance

> *what do you do?*
> *who do you know?*

i tend the orchids
of polluted
gravesites

> well versed in these areas :
> > danger do not trespass
> > contaminated area

where are the profits
left my diamonds   at home
orchids by the fireplace

told them
i was an ally
bow pink color spit

identify as
poet

they said   *first generation are at a disadvantage*
          when parents only speak a language
          that is not english

who told them
who told them that my father left the havana schoolhouse at the age of eight
& never returned

do they know
my brother & i have multiple degrees
& my parents still don't speak   proficient english

i didn't disagree

been to so many marches,
trainings, where are my bedside manners?

>   well versed in these areas :
>   danger do not trespass
>   contaminated area

no one
wants
to

talk
of the
dead

poets
orphaned muses
miscarriages

ancestral repercussions

i feel safe
walking cemeteries
empty church parking lots

no one wants to talk of the dead

the dead don't   have to wear masks
the dead   don't have to   wear masks
the dead don't have to wear masks

How to Play Dead
by Joey Patterson

When you work as a lifeguard, practicing your skills is an essential part
of the job. One of the most important skills to practice is the submerged passive
victim rescue. This scenario is when someone is actively drowning but eventually
swallows too much water, sinks to the bottom of the pool, and goes unconscious.
Although practicing this skill is important, one often overlooked detail is the role
of the victim. In order to give a realistic practice scenario for the lifeguard, the
person playing the victim must also be realistic. In my time as a lifeguard, I've
found that those who play the best victims are often those with prior experience.
Using this as a mental framework could help you in and out of the water. I am
going to teach you how to be a great victim. I am going to teach you how to play
dead.

36

While standing with your feet on the edge of the pool deck, looking out at the reflective blue water, you must be ready to commit. Now, leap high into the air, hold your arms and legs close to your body, and plunge yourself into the role of victim. Before you hit the water, remember to take a deep breath and hold it—just like you did when they would fight when you were younger. Remember the slamming doors, the sudden shouts, gasping, tension. Break the surface with your soft feet: submerge. The water is your bedroom—a locked door keeps you safe. Keep your legs together and push up with your hands to sink. Now, slowly let the air out of your ever filled lungs. Think of the words they never said, the words they stopped saying. *I'm sorry. Are you okay? I love you.* This will help you sink. As you sink slowly to the bottom, exhale more and more. Feel the air escaping your body, allowing you to sink further and further. Remember all the times you wanted to speak up, but couldn't. Sink further. Remember all the times you bit your tongue and held your breath. Sinking, sinking. Ignore the pressure on your chest and in your ears. Further, further. Ignore the chlorine burning your skin. Ignore. Allow your feet to quietly touch the pool floor, like when you tiptoe around the house at night when the TV is on. Remember how good you've gotten at making almost no sound. Then, as you rest on the pool floor, close your eyes if you haven't already. Close your eyes and remember all the times you heard "good children are seen, not heard," and how often it felt like "good children are neither seen nor heard." There's a ten foot wall of water separating you from the nearest person. Think about how good it feels to appear as nothing but a smudge on the pool floor. At this point, you may have one air bubble left in your lungs. The thought of letting it go may be enticing. This is normal. But hold on, the lifeguard is coming to save you. You hear the muffled sounds of whistle blasts and the vacuous plunge of a body into the water, breaking the surface tension. When the lifeguard puts their arm around you, you must not mistake this for the fleeting supportive touch of a mother. You must act boneless, spineless, and lifeless—like being scolded by your father. When you surface in the lifeguard's arms, feel free to take a breath, but remember to stay spineless. Allow your head to bob around, aimless, directionless. It's the lifeguards job to support you. Remember to remain as limp as possible as they strap you into the backboard and hoist you out of the pool. Ignore the sharp velcro cutting into your bare chest. Ignore the head pieces compressing your skull. Remember how good you've gotten at suppressing your pain. Ignore. Ignore. Ignore. You are dead.

After you are on land and drying yourself off, you may hear a lifeguard ask, "are you okay?" But just wait, keep that mouth shut. Most likely, the lifeguard is continuing the scenario, checking for consciousness and practicing CPR on a dummy. Remember that you were only the victim in a hypothetical scenario. But when you go home that night after work, you'll be ready to do it again.

In The Ether
by Lisa Ludden

Often outside yourself, you and I meet
over a glass of water at 2AM.

Your radiant eyes hollow under the paled moon.
All the light you allow.

Why do floors only creak at night, where shadows
lag behind steps, their intensity measuring

the thickness of time? In this pitch blue night
you are clearer than anything I know.

In this shading, I believe in possibilities
beyond what is cellular.

Have you seen her?
The wideness of my daughter's eye belongs to you.

The skies should part
by Brandy Collins

I wasn't "in crisis." I wasn't raised to recognize it, so there was no such thing. It
didn't exist. I listened to Tupac with a large cup of coffee while sitting in daily
traffic en route to a job that was barely sustainable, financially or mentally. That
was making it better than most. I was supposed to be grateful to be here. Of
course, I was not raised to acknowledge a personal crisis.

Black women in my generation weren't given the privilege or permission to be
in crisis. That was meant for white women in Belmont, Calabasas, or some other
town where their skin tone wasn't measured against a paper bag. That was for
the soft, sensitive, and high strung women who actually wanted to respond
when you asked how they were doing. To have a mental breakdown and to cry
out loud meant you should call in sick on a Wednesday so you can catch up on
the laundry while watching your stories. No one should ever see you in distress.

My best friend told me that the first time he saw me cry it scared the shit outta
him. We had known each other for decades and he had only seen me cry once.
Seeing me cry meant something really wrong happened. He was expecting
lightning to crack across a darkening sky. If my tear reached the ground it would
open up the earth and create a crater because there was no way that my eyes
were showing any sign of pain or fear or anguish. Had I been in crisis for so long
that my own open emotional state and vulnerability being exposed to another
human being induced the fear of Armageddon?

When was I supposed to find time for healing and coaxing out trauma that I didn't know was trauma? Was there a handbook? I grew up in the '90s. We didn't have memes and quotes and internet groups of strangers with a daily reminder for us to find healing. We were supposed to go to work, watch Lifetime movies or murder documentaries, drink Rosé, brunch, get pedicurres and make enough money for a singles resort trip to Jamaica. At the very least, you can get a girls trip to Fort Lauderdale or Austin. This was all acceptable. Don't talk about the exhaustion. No one wants to hear your negativity. Think on the bright side.

Then there's moments when you're part of a large family. Raising kids, making everyone's plate at the barbeque, playing dominoes, drinking, and living in the nostalgia of childhood because those were the good old days. You know, sleeping foot to head with your cousins, not because it was a sleepover but because there were thirteen of you living in your grandmother's four-bedroom house. A house that moved in a rhythmic routine of soul music, cleaning and working. Cigarette smoke from the kitchen after ten-hour work shifts. Tea with grape jelly and bacon sandwiches for breakfast. Ramen noodles for lunch. Cinnamon sugar toast for snack. I joke now that grape jelly is part of our oppression.

Then comes the casual mentioning that your stepfather threw you at the wall when you were three years old breaking your femur. "Oh yeah, you remember you had to wear a body cast and be potty trained again?" "Remember that house we had in the suburbs and that time he threw all our stuff in the pool?" "Remember that time when our aunt pulled a gun on our cousin?" "Remember the mystery of who cut our cousin's hair in the middle of the night?" Don't get into a fight and lose. You're going to be sent back out there to fight until you win. Birthday parties that ended with someone drunk and arguing over stolen photo albums and costume jewelry. Casually remember out loud the abusive experiences of childhood.

Understanding and learning healing feels like isolation in the company of other survivors. Survivors? Are we calling ourselves survivors now? I tucked this all away and laughed it off so long because it was normal. Why did you take away my normal? This isn't normal anymore. It wasn't a crisis until now. It was safer in the dark places in my mind. Before I knew that I was supposed to be protected and loved.

I didn't know I was supposed to be protected. The fucking audacity of this knowledge. You mean to tell me that mothers and aunts and fathers and uncles and cousins aren't supposed to treat you this way? The privilege of this feeling. It feels entitled. Maybe the sky does need to crackle when I cry because at this very moment I'm standing in the middle of a crisis I've lived my entire life.

Road Trip
by Carol Moldaw

It rained overnight, refreshing the earth.
The sun made the sky luminous

but the air wasn't yet warm, the leaves
not fully unfurled. It was the height

of the virus, the first wave. With clinics
in seven states closed and ours booked

we were grateful to find one
with an opening within a day's round trip.

I hadn't driven in weeks, for days
hadn't been past the bottom of our drive,

to pick up the paper at 6 and the mail, shorn
of its envelopes outside the house, at 1.

We got a doctor's note in case the state's
border was sealed: "unable to schedule

time-sensitive procedure in-state,
please allow through . . ." —but no one

stopped us and on empty roads we made
good time. Only one hazmat-suited protestor

outside the court-mandated two-block buffer zone
shouldered a sign stapled to a life-size plywood

cross that proclaimed a woman's regret
inevitable. I kept both hands on the wheel

so as not to flip him off as we drove by.
In the parking lot, the cars were spaced

for social distance; her appointment virtually
by phone, each car a semi-private glass-sealed

intake room. I had to pee—what could I do?
I stooped behind a lone thin pine

on the lawn's far edge. At intervals,
the door opened to let someone in or out.

Up and down the path, everyone wore a mask
but with no legal necessity, not yet, to hide.

Black Women Should Choose Silence
by Jenny Mitchell

A hush upon the tongue tastes like control,
even as they curse, men passing in the street,
lips cracked at dim car windows, throwing out abuse.

Silence helps create a minute's space,
blooming with each breath. Their disappointment drops,
word stones they meant to aim. If we answer back,

they hold out a leash, yanked to hear us bark.
It will make them master, power in our pain.
I choose to walk on, calm held like a shield.

Belonging
by Emily Jewett

Growing older was exhausting; not the elongating of my bones, or the tightening of the sinews of muscle as they stretch to keep up, or the pains that plagued me every night in my shins and led to a prolonged clumsy phase in which most of my limbs were a mottled watercolor of bruises from tripping over things or smacking my newly long limbs on things. The exhausting part was watching the way men looked at me change. It used to be with benevolence, with soft eyes and softer smiles. That softness faded into stiff frigidity as soon as I began to change, to begin the long process of becoming a woman instead of a child, their eyes now raking over my body and lingering in places they'd barely even noticed before. It was like they were devouring me alive, blood and plasma running down their chins. They haven't stopped since.

I was first catcalled when I was freshly thirteen. We used to have a Subway a ten-minute walk away from my dad's house in the suburbs, combined with the convenience store attached to our local gas station. My dad slipped me a twenty and told me to go pick us up some sandwiches. I was wearing jean shorts that grazed the top of my skinny thighs and a baby pink t-shirt as I walked down the road. A car honked behind me, and as I turned to look, a man made an obscene gesture at me out of the window of his black sedan. You know the gesture: a peace sign held up to his mouth while he waggled his disgusting tongue. I didn't know what it meant but I walked faster. When I got home, I mimicked the gesture and asked my stepmom what it was. She visibly paled and asked me how I knew that. That was how I learned what oral sex was and that a grown man wanted to do it to my thirteen-year-old, not yet through puberty.

The second time I was barely fourteen. I was walking my dog home from the coffee shop near my mom's house. I was too young to drink coffee, so I would walk down from my house and get a two-dollar Italian soda with my babysitting money. It was our Thursday ritual that summer. Another honk. I pulled my earbud out and turned to see a man in a red pickup. He yelled, "Hey, sexy!" and then sped down the road before I could even reply. I clutched my dog's leash tighter and fought back the panic that rose in my chest. I looked down at my linen shorts and my long tank top and wondered if it was my fault. Maybe I couldn't dress for the weather when I was alone. From then on, I wore jeans on my coffee shop walks. Later that day, my boyfriend texted me that we needed to break up because he cheated on me and couldn't live with it on his conscience. What cheating is in a sexless relationship between two incoming high school freshmen I still don't know, but I remember that day in vivid detail. I was objectified by a man and then cast aside by a boy.

My adult body still isn't mine. When I was walking down Mission Boulevard to go pick up a bottle of wine for girl's night, a group of men rolled down their windows and screamed, "Show us your pussy!" as they drove by. I was wearing mom jeans. Logically, if that line had worked, they would've been long gone by the time I shimmied out of the constricting denim. They didn't think they'd actually see me naked; they just wanted me to know that they wanted to. That my body was theirs to consume with starving eyes, ravenous for their pound of flesh.

My junior year, my friends Colin and Xavier walked my roommate Cam and me home from a party, taking us along the dark back streets. A car stopped next to us, and two men invited Cam and me into the backseat to "have some fun." Xavier put his arm in front of me as Colin stepped in front of Cam, wielding his skateboard as some sort of weapon. Luckily he didn't have to use it. The car drove away and I laughed it off but sat with the "what if" scenarios later that night as I tried to find some peace in sleep. If my male friends hadn't been there, if it were just Cam and me alone on the unlit street in the dead of night, I don't know what would've happened. Maybe I would've ended up in the backseat against my wishes and then god knows where. Maybe I'd be one of those girls Netflix makes true crime documentaries about, found decomposing with a raw-red slashed throat in some forgotten ditch, the maggots and flies making their home in the gaping holes in my rotting body. Maybe it wasn't an actual invitation, just another reminder that my own self doesn't belong to me.

When I told my guy friend I was bisexual, he put a hand on my thigh, bare in my flowing mini skirt, higher up than I would've liked, and said with a squeeze into my yielding flesh, "Emily, that's hot." Even my sexuality isn't mine. In his head, my sexual identity existed for him to fetishize, to imagine us in a hypothetical threesome, me and some other poor girl writhing atop him. We wouldn't be enjoying each other, no. We'd be performing for him, letting him memorize each motion, each moan, to keep in his head the next time his hand found itself down his pants.

My first out of body experience happened when I was eighteen. It was October of 2017. A man who was my boyfriend at the time, my very first boyfriend, was having sex with my body while my consciousness floated somewhere else. I said no. I did. "I came all the way to visit you, the least you could do is try," he said. I could feel the tears on my face but nothing else but sharp pain and a ceaseless hollowness. That hollowness lingers whenever I remember. I left my body on its own and let it suffer, let it become his, while I was somewhere else. A meadow with the sun gently kissing my rosy and youthful cheeks, the grass nestled softly beneath my tired head. Under the stars in the middle of the desert, watching the constellations form before my sleepy eyes. On a boat floating in the ocean while the waves rock me to sleep, dolphins nuzzling my fingertips while my hand skims the top of the peaceful water. I was there, in my brain's version of paradise, while my corporeal form remained in hell. I floated above her, the physical her who was once me but wasn't anymore, the true me lingering anywhere else. I came back to her at the end, when it finally stopped, and stumbled to the bathroom to clean the blood off of the inside of my thighs. I caressed my own cheek, my palm migrating over my mouth to silence my gasping breaths.

Giving myself willingly makes me a whore. "I just didn't think you'd be like that," my college boyfriend said to me, his hands resting on the steering wheel as he drove us to dinner at some new cafe. "Like what?" I asked, fingers fidgeting with the hem of the dress I chose specifically for this date, hoping he'd tell me I was pretty. "Like a whore," he said, nonchalantly, as if what he was saying wasn't atrocious. We broke up for a time when I went abroad in the fall of my junior year, then briefly reunited when I returned in the spring. He couldn't get past the fact that I slept with someone else when we weren't together. He shamed me for it constantly, until I became numb to the sharp incisors of the bite of his words. I hardly spoke up, even though I knew he had been fucking some sweet, innocent freshman when I was gone, whispering that he loved her in her ear when he always planned on drawing me back to him. In his head he was comparing me to her. Her, the naive, young girl in her first semester of school; me, the experienced slut letting any and every man inside her while traipsing around Europe. The European man told me I was beautiful, kissed me like I was the only thing that mattered to him, and held me against his chest all night, limbs entangled like tree roots that grew for decades wrapped around each other, while I fell into a comfortable and dreamless sleep as he whispered in my ear in a lyrical language I did not understand. I haven't slept like that in a long time. I wonder if I ever will again.

I never knew that my second ex coerced me until I thought about it years after. "Come on, let's just fool around," he would say to me over and over, when I told him I didn't want to have sex, mere moments after he first kissed me and mere weeks after the theft of my virtue by another man who also didn't like the sound of the word "no." "Fooling around" very quickly became sex, before my brain could even fully register what was happening. I just said "yes" because that's all I knew how to say. I didn't want to lose him, I can't stand losing people, and I knew quickly he'd lose interest in anyone who refused him. "No" left my vocabulary until I woke up one day, twenty years old and bitter, because my body had never been mine since the first moment it entered the sexual realm.

Even when my body is mine, it isn't. When my body doesn't look like the world tells me it should, I feel broken. I look at myself in the mirror before my shower and shudder. Cellulite decorates me. It's a secondary sex characteristic in women. It's normal. Yet, when I look at mine, I don't eat. My record was twenty-four hours, which in my mind felt weak. I could've gone on longer, I really could've. I would either do that, or upon deeply rare occasions, stick my own fingers so far down my throat that vomit would suddenly appear in the toilet bowl. I never told anyone, not even my best friends. I felt embarrassed. I didn't want to add to the burden that my friendship already was. It was just another heavy suitcase to throw atop the cart full of baggage, piled a mile high into the stratosphere.

I don't do that anymore, thanks to a carefully crafted speech from my therapist I conjure in my mind when I think about starving myself or throwing up, about how my body is the reason I live, the reason I survive, and it is beautiful regardless of what others have said to me; but the frightening behavior was a more frequent occurrence in the past than I want to admit. I wanted to be thin, to be the beautiful girl men want; to be the hourglass; the smooth Barbie they jack off to night after night so I can one day be loved.

I want to slice myself up with a carving knife like I'm the roast beef station on some horrible, purgatorial cruise and serve my body, raw and full of gristle, to the men who tore me apart. I want to force them to eat it, to choke it down, to taste the blood and marrow and fat with every swallow. Maybe if I'm feeling benevolent I'll give them salt and pepper to sprinkle over my eviscerated tissue. I want them to feast on my body, to gag and vomit with every revolting bite, to know that this is what they've done with me. The men in the cars, the man who sexually assaulted me, the man who broke my self worth and abused me beyond recognition. They ripped me to shreds, so let them fork the pieces of me into their greedy and glib mouths if that's what they wanted so fucking badly. Is that not what they deserve for what they've done to me?

Life in the Forever Fires:
Toward Serenity in the Apocalypse
by Kailyn McCord
Previously published in LitHub.

I was on a plane when the Tubbs fire burned. This was 2017. A rumor ran through the airport that our flight was one of only a dozen to land that day, that the remaining hundreds of others were canceled, diverted, sent to destinations the people in them had not elected when they boarded for takeoff. We angled out of the air, which I felt in the belly, just as all I could see through my little window was a strange, white diffusion, an infinite nothing that held us, weightless, until the runway rushed up fast and the carriage of the airplane sank heavy onto its wheels. I was back for a visit, and this was not the California I knew.

A year later, the Camp Fire smoked Oakland in for a month (the fire's official name, "Camp," although everyone I know refers to it by the name of the town it took, Paradise, like something from a bad fairy tale). I'd moved back by then, was living in a small blue house in the foothills of the city, my childhood home, the only place in Oakland I could afford. A listless haze stretched across a weak neon sun, the disc hanging like a dim button in the span. The view from the higher streets I knew from girlhood, its geography as reliable as any morning fog, was gone: no glimmering bay, no city skyline obscuring the ocean, no bridges crossing the water. The mornings dawned one after the next in opaque, limpid pinks, a curtain that disappeared the world somewhere off in the middle distance. It was something like what we remembered from Tubbs, but not exactly, still its own discreet event.

When, come the following fall, the Kingcade fire bloomed across the north bay, I wasn't in California. I was at a residency in Wyoming. I called my partner each night, asked how he was, asked for his accounts of what was happening. At first he talked about his feelings, the same feelings I was having, too – shock, worry, an eerie itch that some fundamental stuff of what assured his world was under threat. As the days went on, the tone with which he spoke began to ease, something like normalcy creeping in. *It's fire season again,* he said, a little earlier, bigger and faster, but basically, essentially, like last year.

We adapt so quickly. By fractional adjustments we arrive at a completely new understanding of ourselves, and by the stepwise process manage to do so without ever having realized any departure in the first place. Like the frog in water, temperature rising all the time, we repeat this phrase (of a pandemic, of climate events) *new normal,* as if by its repetition we can will it into being, as if, by insisting we are already adjusted, we will be able to forget whatever normal once was, ignore whatever long distance we're come from that place.

Here is what they don't tell you about the frogs: prior to the experiment, each specimen was lobotomized. The parts of their brains that would sense distress, or danger, that would trigger their reflex to jump to the glinting edge of the pot and, if they were lucky, escape to the cool safety of the countertop: these were gone. And so 2020 came to California, and the sky filled with ash, and I was left wondering whether I still had the parts necessary for survival.

*

I know California fires. In 1991, a firestorm tore through Oakland the likes of which the modern age had never seen. It surrounded completely the house I live in, but did not burn it down. I lived in it then, too; I was four, and when my parents evacuated us – when they stood at the second story windows of their friends' house, and clutched each other, and watched the hills go orange – they were sure our house was gone. That they were wrong would be the relief of a lifetime: a yard of ash the following afternoon, the scorched roofs of the neighbors, and then around the bend, their own soot stained miracle standing in the grey.

I have been writing about that fire, about California fires, for years now. In the basement-turned-apartment of that same house, I sit, and think, and read thousands of pages of government reports and first-hand eye witness accounts of the 1991 fire. I learn about the meteorology behind the Santa Ana winds. I call experts, the authors of papers I've tried to decipher and can't, and cajole them into explaining their work to me over the phone. I pour through Wikipedia, trying to parse the basics of what qualifies an event as a firestorm, or a conflagration, or this new word we're seeing more of all the time, "complex." I watch fire officials in tiny videos on Twitter, listen as they explain that "complex" is the word for a series of fires in a given region, classified by "similar characteristics, starting time, and geography." These officials offer the definition with stalwart authority, like it is some solution, like they are saying something other than *when there are this many, we run out of names.*

I track lists through the years, these lists ordered by structure loss or death count or acres burned. The top of almost every one of these lists, now, is a fire from the last five years. For nearly thirty years before that, the top of many, if not most, was '91.

I do this from a place of compulsion. Whether in writing, or in any other investigative tear, I do it from the blood, because, as another Californian once said, "In times of trouble, I had been trained since childhood, read, learn, work it up, got to the literature." It is a skillset I've honed through years of higher education, critical thinking, at seminars and conferences and retreats. What is my command over my own life besides my ability to understand it? Understanding, a dissection: this is what I do best.

What I am saying is that I should be okay with what is happening in California. I have, by increments, by the salve of information, adjusted myself to the temperature of the water. I should understand that what we're seeing has been fated for a long time. Because I do understand that, and because to me, understanding means solution, my own persistent discomfort is a mystery.

What I have not examined, not really, is the impulse that starts the compulsive researching, thinking, writing, the instinctual seed, and whether the long years of obsession are actually an answer to what starting gun compels them forward. It's hard to pin point, that moment, as fleeting as it is, in part because I've been kicking hard away from it for a long time now. But there's something under there, some feeling all this cerebrum is working so hard to shore up.

*

People are more comfortable thinking themselves the arbiters of their own fortunes, rather than living every day with the close, clear reality that they are, broadly speaking, at the mercy of something larger. It's why we insist on normalcy as we do, on narrative, on the familiar characters and the basics of what drive them. It's why I gravitate toward information, toward "the literature," the mechanism by which I happily conflate knowledge with control, by which I build a narrative from the past, and try to imprint it over what I think of the future.

We see this construction of narrative, and the habit of putting human agency at its center, even in the very most singular images of fire: the firefighter as he descends the ladder, exhausted, blackened but successful, his heroism over his shoulder in the form of a child or a pet or a fellow fireman. If he is not successful, and especially if he is lost to the fight, his failure is reassured by a grateful community, his memory immortalized with speeches and statues. I hold no position on whether firefighters are heroes or not, but rather my aim is to point out that, when we focus on fire, what we highlight is a person's ability to fight it, or when they cannot, our ability to appropriately revere their memory. We fit fire into the human narrative; we emphasize our power over it; we mold the reality of such an elemental force into something over which we have a mechanism, any mechanism, of control.

The end of the Didion quote: "Information was control." It that true? I've had my share of twelve step meetings. I've thought a lot about control, about attachment, about what it means to love with no guarantees. I am coming to understand that, no matter how diligently I try to acclimatize, no matter how meticulously I follow every kernel of information back to its source, I will never be comfortable with what is happening. This is my home; these are the people I love best in the world, and not a single thing I know about normalcy, or narrative, applies to us now.

Yesterday, I sat in the backyard. Ash fell from the sky like a fine, light snow, settled on the broad leaves of a squash plant gone sickly green against the

46

orange air. My garden hadn't seen the sun in days, and I didn't know when it would again, but I watered, swept the deck, set the tools back in their corner. I went inside and pulled a polyester duffle bag out from under the bed. More than thirty years I've been a Californian, and I'd never packed a go-bag before.

It's a strange thing, to walk through the space you live in and try to decide which parts of it you'll want most when the rest are gone. I looked up some lists on the internet. I added several of their suggestions (clothing, snacks, documents, cash). When the essentials were accounted for, I pushed them aside to make room for the disembodied middle drawer of my writing desk, which I maneuvered, full of notebooks, beyond the open zipper and into the belly of the bag. I'd built the desk more than a decade ago, with my partner, back when we were barely more than children. It's made of old growth redwood, pieces once near-rotting in his salvage pile, now planed and sanded fine, a relic of human achievement in its own right.

With the drawer, the bag is bulky, has a strange non-bag shape to it when I set it by the door to the kitchen, which is where it will stay for the rest of the season, or the year, or however long we wake each morning and see the very air reassuring us that normalcy is a dangerous proposition. At night, when the world seems almost familiar for the fact that we cannot see the sky, I lay awake and stare at the open space left in the desk, its dark, square absence stretching back into nothing. I listen to my partner's heart beat under my ear, in his chest, count his breaths as they come, one after the next. There's little else to do, I've found, at the end of the world.

Gender Change Instructions
by Jo Unruh

Published by The Supreme International Authority Extraordinaire on Alleviating Confusion and Telling it Like it Is

Congratulations! You finally realized that life is too short and you couldn't make your gender dysphoria go away, no matter how hard you tried to find that magic light switch. By now, you've come out to your family and friends, you've gone through 4 to 9 therapists in the last year, and you've decided to take the leap and transition genders. We are here to say GOOD FOR YOU!! You're about to embark on a second puberty, or what we like to call, "one of the wildest rides of your freakin' life!" Enjoy!

***WARNING**: THESE INSTRUCTIONS ARE FOR CHANGING GENDERS FROM MALE TO FEMALE—
NOT TO BE CONFUSED WITH OUR SEPARATE INSTRUCTIONS FOR CHANGING FROM FEMALE TO MALE. FAILURE TO COMPLY WITH THIS WARNING COULD RESULT IN INADVERTENT LOSS OR GAIN OF SEX ORGANS. ***

STEP 1: Buckle the fuck up, buttercup.

STEP 2: Be prepared to constantly field intimate questions about your sexual orientation, and about your private body parts that are also likely the greatest visible artifacts of your gender dysphoria. The most common questions you will face are:

1. Does this mean you are gay?
2. So, are you going to cut off your penis?
3. I don't get it…how will you have sex?

STEP 3: Go back to STEP 2 and start taking stock of your answers to the most common questions you receive. We highly suggest you talk your answers over with your therapist, family therapist, coke dealer (but please not your meth dealer), couples' therapist, Doctor of Psychology, spiritual advisor, tantric sex guru, and psychiatrist. You will need to have well developed answers for later steps.

STEP 4: HRT Informed consent: You'll need to sign lots of papers before starting estrogen and t-blockers, stating that you've been informed of all the risks. You're too excited to read all those pages anyways, so we've summarized the informed consent documents for you here in three succinct points:

1. Say goodbye to your little swimmers
2. Read about breast cancer, 'cause ya might get it now
3. You will become addicted to chocolate, pickles, and crying

STEP 5: By the time your nipples start hurting, you're probably thinking of having your facial hair removed, if you haven't already. Three things: aloe, aloe, and aloe. Find yourself a nice electrologist, because for 50 to 100 hours of your life she will double as your fourth primary source of psychological therapy while she's looking up your nose and using a 23rd century torture machine to pluck out every single follicle of hair on your little chinny-chin-chin. Just be thankful you're not Italian. And if you are Italian, we're so sorry.

> NOTE on Step 5: You're likely going to have to do this hair removal thing all over again for all that hair down unda', too, if you catch our drift, so even more reason to find the right electrologist. If you find someone you like, ask her if she's comfortable staring at the junk you hate. Just sayin'.

STEP 6: So you want to have that Adam's apple reduced, do you? Wonderful! Find yourself a nice plastic surgeon, but buyer beware: you'll most likely have to sit through multiple briefings examining all of the "ultra-masculine features" of your face, in an effort to convince you that you'll never "pass" as a woman, unless you let the surgeon's masterful hands give you full facial feminization surgery, for the low low price of your kid's college education. And even after you don't splurge on full FFS on the first pitch, he'll joke at your Adam's apple surgery post-op that he'll see you back in 6 months for a new face. And that he'll even give you a discount if you purchase a new set of tits to go along with the renovated forehead and jawline.

STEP 6: This is what we like to call the "recalibrate your expectations phase." You'll be feeling pretty good about yourself by now. Confident, really, especially since your doctor hopefully has taken enough vials of blood from you that he/she/they have your hormones dialed in to match the levels of a cis-female. You start experimenting more with your hair, makeup, and wardrobe, and you even get gendered correctly sometimes. Hooray! Well guess what, friend. Here's where you will also start to notice more than ever how disgusting the gender you just left behind can be. And you pathetically thought women were overreacting before. Fun how that works, isn't it? Be prepared to get stares of confusion, disgust, longing, perversion, and disapproval from nearly every single man over 30—no, let's make that 25—you ever pass by. If you're lucky, you'll only get followed by one creep the first time you go to Target in your new but tastefully subdued women's clothing.

STEP 7: So you're really doin' it now. You've survived at least a year of HRT, a steady stream of no less than 2 transition-related appointments a week, and you're ready to go for bottom surgery. At this point, you hate your penis more than ever, and you're sick of having to tape it up between your legs just to wear a goddamn pair of cute pants without having some awkward bulge to go along with your new bra that helps make your oddly shaped man boobs look more like real boobs. Here's where you're going to need to refer back to the answers you catalogued during STEP 2, because guess what, for your new vagina, there are more options than on a brand-new Lincoln! Move over, Matthew McConoughey. For completing this step, please see our other, comprehensive guide on vaginoplasty, vulvoplasty, and everything in between. Your new female hardware is so complex we decided it needs its own standalone guide rather than being included in this one. Please note: that guide is not suitable for younger audiences, straight white men (even though you used to claim to be one), and adults that did not graduate into the new millennium.

STEP 8: If you've made it this far, kudos to you. You are one of few to have successfully crossed over. Doesn't it feel grand? And for that, society will grant you a CONGRATULATORY GOLD STAR. Just kidding. At best, you might get a decent job to pay off all the debt you're now in from steps 1 through 7, and your parents still talk to you. At worst, well, we don't want to discourage you.

BUT in all seriousness, your journey will teach you the true meaning of love, and how to unlock love's power. And this rare knowledge, friends, will make you a superhero.

Welcome to the Unicorn Club, bitch. Don't fuck it up.

Scene XXXI
by Loisa Fenichell

And suddenly, like a break in the pink sun, I think it must be over, this spell of
grief so shredded even in appeasing light. I tell those who visit look, today I even
like my curves, today, my arms, the many ways in which they spell out words
like senses of desire. I can tell they don't believe me. How they still see me in the
kitchen, baking with the drowned. I explain to them that it was a mistake, I made
a mistake, to have missed him so. The way his mouth held itself open to the
night, his breath smokey, his breath mixing with stale bedroom air. The way his
tailless cat perched on his lap. How he held her, how he stroked her, even across
her absent tail. The visitors laugh when I say look, I'm ready for love. They tell
me, you had it, the exclamation point caught in their throats like lost weeds. They
don't say, you had it and you lost it, but I can tell what they mean. I am good at
interpreting their silences, their gaps in conversation broad as turnstiles. Even
with this absence hanging over me, an open field, I think I am good.

Private

take this body
by Jenny Qi

there are 30 trillion cells birthed from the first ancestral cell in this body.
every single cell has inherited the same instructions for mapping this body.

what is it like to move about the world without feeling weight — every choice
not choice heavy with millennia of blood blades flesh trapping this body.

when I was five, a boy brought a model heart to show and tell. blue beads
rattled against plastic veins. my heart pumps blue blood enwrapping this body.

once I was a child in the library, a man stooped to ask for help finding books.
when my mother found me, I felt the newness of danger overlapping this body.

Parravani and Me: An Exercise
by Jennifer Sapio

*"Our lives were a jumble… We shared everything until there was nothing of our single
selves left. It was my task in grieving her to unravel the tight, prickly braid of memory
rope we'd woven –to unwind and unwind and unwind until I was able to take my strand
and lay it out beside the length that was hers" (6).*

What a powerful image of sisters braided together like a rope in the
author's memory. I think of braiding my sister's hair when we were children. I
learned to French braid with the older girls at daycare when we went to La Petite
off Anderson Lane, but to this day, my sister still can't braid.

I also think about money trees, whose trunks are woven together when
the stalks are young and supple, flexible, still able to bend and adapt. When one
of my money trees was struggling, I noticed that the elastic bands that had held
the braided trunks in place was suffocating the plant, growing into the flesh
where it had outgrown its previous restraints. Out of bounds. Colored outside
the lines. Eventually, one of the three stalks died, and I had to remove its dry,
brown corpse from the pot, unwinding its brothers and sisters, snakelike, from
their wombmates so that they weren't beautiful anymore, but free.

"I thought my occasional need to surrender to a pill was justified. But
that need was also a warning: I was closer to being Cara than I knew" (23).

This is a nice moment of self-reflection, a palimpsest of sorts. The nar-
rator lets us know a previous mindset "I thought," followed by the reality, a
"warning." This is a significant part of the work of memoir writers, yes? Repre-
senting the self-reflective journey we've experienced on the page.

Specifically, talking about drug use is hard for an academic, or for a
family with a legacy of substance abuse. The lines, as Parravani suggests here,
do indeed becoming blurry between who's using and who's abusing, justifica-

tions and blame pointing every which direction. I remember feeling intensely judgmental of my sister's heroin use although I was happy to celebrate "Tequila Tuesdays" with her for an entire spring, that semester I dropped out of college, and she was finishing high school.

Wouldn't I have ended up like Sarah if I had a big sister like me, too?

"Dad walked to a chair and put his head in his hands. 'Girls, two girls.' He shook his head. 'Can we send one back?'" (31).

I've heard the story so many times I can almost see it. My mom says that when my sister was born, and she had colic, she would cry for hours, for days. She apparently cried for months. One night, as the story goes, my mom was crying alone in her bedroom as I sneaked in to comfort her. Stroking my mother's hair, I tell her, "I think it's time we take the baby back to the hospital."

Every time we heard the story, I would laugh. But Sarah wouldn't.

"His abuse raised the bar on what was tolerable. There was nothing we weren't prepared to take from a man and nothing we didn't dish out in return" (34).

It's easy to tell stories about my dad hurting me, or my sister, or my step-dad, or my boyfriends. It's harder to be honest about how abuse can transform you into an abuser, too.

You can dish it out, but you can't take it, they say:

the time I threw my phone across the room; it hit the wall and shattered into pieces

the time I picked up a dining room chair and dashed it on the floor

the time I sat in a room with two people I was sleeping with, and lied to them both

the time I rammed my car into the back of his blue Ford Mustang

the time I threatened to shove my sister out of the car on Bee Caves Road

the time she called the cops on me because I wouldn't leave her house

the multiple times I threatened to kill her boyfriends

the time I hit him, open-palmed in the face, before he got out his gun

the time I said I hoped he died with a thousand needles in his arm, but I meant her

"My sister, my twin, we fought like alley cats and then walked down the street together, wherever it was we were living, holding hands. We tangled each other's hair, bloodied each other's noses, bit and scratched each other. We knew who we were: We were best friends. We were enemies. We were all we had" (62).

52

Holding hands, she writes. It's not the only time Parravani mentions the intimate gesture in her memoir. So passionate. I think of holding hands with lovers, not family. Or, with children, for safety, when crossing a busy street.

My mom routinely tells another story, perhaps as an antidote to the one where I ask to take my sister back to the hospital. In this one, my mom is at work, and my sister and I are at La Petite Academy. Our pre-school classes are divided by age. My little sister Sarah is actually in a different building. I'm in C-building, and we have our own big-kid playground, separated from the little ones by a chain-link fence.

Mom says she got a call from the daycare director, who was nearly crying herself. Apparently, my sister and I had found one another on opposite sides of the fence and grasped hands through the gaps in the wire. They couldn't separate us.

"We were all we had." So matter of fact. We must have known then, young as we were, that neither parent would claim us full-time. We'd have part-time lives, passed with our suitcases between Round Rock and Austin on IH-35, all the tangles and bits only fully shared with one another.

"Cara stood up and grabbed my hand, pulled me up off the sofa, and twisted my fingers back against my wrist until I cried out in pain. Our boyfriends looked worried. 'You're dumped,' she said to her boyfriend, 'for kissing my sister.' Cara undid her hair from the style I'd made for her and shook her long locks over her shoulder, dramatically exposing her true identity.

Our boyfriends sat stunned. The blinking blue screen of the television flickered on their faces.

'Whatever,' one of our boyfriends said to the other. He got up to leave. 'They're the same chick anyway'" (68).

This is how it started:
Yes, I had kissed his little brother, too. That is true.
So, when my boyfriend picked me up from the airport, on one of my trips home to Austin from Barnard, and told me that he had kissed my sister while I was away, there was part of me that thought we were just even.
This is how it's going:
On the day of the intervention, my sister got the handler guy to agree to pick some of her things up on the way to rehab. I followed behind them in his car all the way to my ex-boyfriend's house. The one who had picked me up from the airport with the Pok-e-Jo's Barbeque and Yellow Tail to soften the blow about the errant smooch. Turns out it wasn't one spit swap. He picked her, and she picked him back.

"Stealing didn't only go one way. I felt free to help myself to anything that was hers as well. I took from her often" (89).

Eric.
Jeff.

"I was under the impression, the deluded perspective of the desperate, that the more money we threw at the problem of Cara's addiction and despair, the more likely it was that she'd recover...

At the baggage terminal, overcome with drugs, she fell flat on her face onto the airport floor, chipping her front teeth and blackening one eye. This was how she arrived into the custody of her handler from The Meadows, like a has-been prizefighter gone down in the first round" (111).

Parravani's delusion and desperation matches her sister's in this scene. Christa and her family pour money at the problem, and Cara shoves drugs in her face. Excellent juxtaposition.

I had an epiphany when I read this passage.

See, on this one particularly rough night, my sister apparently blacked out walking across the street into our driveway. I had woken up to the sound of her screaming and stumbling up the stairs to her room above mine in the "Rabbit Hutch" on Stratford Lane. My sister and I lived in a separate building on the compound my mother's new husband owned, which overlooked Lake Austin and the city skyline. I knew nobody else could hear her wailing, so I would have to help, which irritated the hell out of me at the time for a couple of reasons. First, I was disgusted with my sister's drugging and drinking although I was pretty guilty of those indiscretions myself. Second, a couple of nights earlier, my sister had brought two guys home to her bedroom above mine, and I heard the three of them in the shower, to my horror.

I was still slut-shaming my sister in my own mind when I awoke to her cries a couple of nights later. When I opened my bedroom door, I saw bloody handprints making their way up the stairs. When I found my sister, she was screaming in the bathroom, staring at her bloody face in the mirror.

"Am I ugly," she cried. "My face, my fucking face."

I only just realized that it was my own ugliness, like seeing myself in a mirror, that so disgusted me about my sister. At the time, I, too, was fucking two guys. It seems delusional to me now how proud of myself I was that it just wasn't at the same time.

And how desperate we both were to need so much more than any one person could give us.

"Cara was raped only four weeks after Jedediah and I were married; the rape became part of our marriage. Jedediah would lie beside me most nights. Or we only spooned, him behind me, his arms wrapped around my waist. We could have been brother and sister. On the rare occasions when we'd begin making love, I'd close my eyes and imagine that I was my sister. I could feel her assailant on top of me. Jedediah was gentle, but to give to him, I had to float out of body. I kept my floating a secret...

I thought: when Cara dies I'm going to get a divorce. When Cara dies, I'm going to move to New York City. When Cara dies, I'm going got be very thin" (146-147).

This kind of planning for the death of the addict seems to be typical in families like Parravani's and mine.

My sister didn't die, but her illness changed my life.

I met my future husband in group therapy. I showed him a picture of my sister to make sure he'd never met her, or slept with her, before. He said he hadn't. So, we got married. My sister was not the maid of honor at my wedding. My sister was not present when my son was born.

I imagined getting a call with the news that she was dead every day for about a decade. I wondered if they sent someone to the door. I imagined a eulogy I would give.

My sister was my whole world.

But since my sister was sick, I made a new family. I created a world in which she didn't exist. When she got better and came back, I lived in a new house with a new man and a new body.

When I had asked my ex why he chose her over me, he said he couldn't get it up because I was too fat. So, I gained a hundred pounds. My sister wouldn't even recognize me when she saw me again. She didn't die, but maybe part of me did.

"My teeth became loose" (190).

Parravani's passive voice here is stunning.

My belly became fat.
My ass became pimply.
My hair became gray.
My finger became broken.
My heels became crusty.
My legs became hairy.
My vagina became torn.
My breasts became swollen.
My chin too became hairy.
My neck and shoulders became sore.
My skin became dry.
My lips became cracked.
My eyes became bloodshot.
My arm and ribs became tattooed.
My cheeks became wet.
My heart became numb.

Trio
by Megan Noble

June, 2018.

It was a Friday evening in the East Bay hills and the three of us stood by the door as Easton leashed Stryker, his German Shepard, for a walk. Next to Stryker, Easton looked like trouble. At 6'4", over a foot taller than me, Easton had gotten in a habit of slowing his stride to match that of mine and Emmitt's — the two of us taking our time on uneven sidewalk that petered off into nothing as the streets narrowed. The studs in Easton's ears sparkled in the afternoon sun, and his right forearm, gripping Stryker's leash, featured the wild eyes of a tiger, red and bloodthirsty. Crawling up from the tiger's tail, onto his elbow, were a handful of scarlet roses. Emmitt, closer to my height, made up for inches with curly red hair and a loud laugh that heightened the easy quiet Easton and I lived in.

The three of us passed through the ever-open gates of the cemetery and Stryker lay down over ledgers and well-watered grass. The boys followed in suit, slumping in the green. We'd been debating, pausing briefly to smile at the older couples walking through the neighborhood, as the boys tag-teamed our argument as usual, laying out the reasons why 'objectivity' was something to strive toward. I pushed back, believing full-heartedly that *there's no such thing as objective*. I appealed to Easton's art: "How would you paint from an 'objective' perspective?" Easton conceded, but Emmitt persisted. Clarified. Said that *decisions* should be made as objectively as possible, *reporting* should be done as objectively as possible; our individual perspectives shouldn't cloud *fact*. We rattled off our points and, eventually, came to a stalemate.

"You know," Emmitt said. "The only reason we keep you around is because you can have intelligent conversations with us."

Easton nodded and scratched Stryker's back legs.

Truthfully, I felt special, not insulted, by this testament to our friendship. At the pool, Easton was formidable; an intensity of silence followed his every footstep. He kept to himself and constantly chose the chair in the corner of the guardroom. Emmitt, on the other hand, a cynic of other sorts, expressed his distaste for people differently. At the pool, he criticized the too-talkative, the over-sharers and overly optimistic, often mocking me for my "fake" enthusiasm while teaching swim lessons. The two of them openly hated people, but they'd let me in, allowed me to join their exclusive club and listen to music I didn't understand, like Death Grips and $uicideBoy$.

My mouth twisted into a smile at the backhanded compliment, willing to accept whatever compliments they might give. And though our argument about objectivity was dead, Emmitt eventually led our conversation to familiar territory: feeling like shit, feeling anxious or depressed.

In these moments, I often felt like an outsider, not sharing their experience with the same intensity, not always sure of what to say, not understanding the full force of Easton's words last summer when we'd laid together, my arms folded neatly across his chest, and he said: "We can be as close as physically possible, take you and me for example, and still be completely alone in our heads."

"Do you guys wanna meditate?" I asked.

Like so many things I suggested — watching the sunset, going on a hike — I thought they'd laugh. But this time, they agreed.

Crossing their legs.

Bowing their heads.

Closing their eyes.

Emmitt on the downslope of the hill, the bleached hairs of his elbows resting against knees; Easton with his back hunched, arms outstretched like a zombie, the newest addition to his sleeve still covered in saran wrap.

I watched them, not participating myself so I could lead them through the meditation. And as they sat in the cemetery, breathing deeply while Stryker's tongue darted in and out of his mouth, I thought about the summer before with Easton. When we lay beneath white sheets in a white bedroom.

It had been a month of me slowly working up my confidence to talk to him. I'd flirt with him over banana pancakes in the guard room, fawn over the fact that he'd take a leftovers box out of the trash and walk across the deck to put it in the compost, and yearn to know him after we were paired together in a staff training, wading in the corner of the pool, talking about the split between our minds and our hearts: we both wanted to pursue the arts — for him, the visual, for me, the written — but was it feasible? We were both here, at the pool, summer after summer, after all, because stability had its own allure.

When we ended up in the white bedroom together, it wasn't really that I wanted sex. I wanted to know the thoughts of the quietest boy in the room. I wanted to hear him say that yes, choosing art was a "feast or famish" type of deal, but that it was worth it to at least try. I wanted to be inspired by his bravery, by his rejection of the path I saw ahead of me after college.

Later that night, after he'd asked me what was on my mind, after we began contemplating consciousness, I would say: "I think that to be alive means to feel." And he'd agree, mention his depression. Say that it was the absence of feeling, it was being *comfortably numb*, but that these days, he wanted to feel everything.

What it felt like to drown and be revived.

What it felt like to kill a man.

Does that scare you? he'd ask. *No*, I'd say. And I meant it. I'd fall asleep that night, beneath white sheets, entangled in his white arms, and feel safe spooned up against him, not scared.

*

Maybe I knew I was doing it at the time, but I really don't think I did. Something had shifted this summer, and it felt like Emmitt was my only way to get to Easton. We became friends, Emmitt and me, the kind that texted each other constantly, that FaceTimed from separate states. That hung out after work, sitting in cars parked at the top of the hill trapped in fog, talking about everything on our minds. He'd pass me on the pool deck and whisper in my ear: "You're distracting me from my job." And I'd shake my head, but smile, and tell him there were people in the pool, *watch them*. And he'd laugh, stalk back to the guard stand in his black and white checkered Vans. It was hard to know whether he really wanted me or whether this was just how he was. His eyes were hidden from me beneath a pair of Ray Bans — red, like his hair.

But then, Emmitt would be calling me dumb because I didn't know dolphins had echolocation. He'd tell me I had mosquito bites for boobs and I'd tell him to fuck off.

That was the thing about Emmitt: one minute he was shocking me with kindness, and the next he was shocking me with cruelty. But whether in texts or in whispers at work, I caught and cradled every one of the compliments he tossed my way, amassing so many I was unable to decode which made me feel good and which didn't, using them to fill in the gaps in attention I lacked from Easton, eagerly receiving it from Emmitt, still unwavering in my pursuit of Easton, who hadn't given me any real sense of intimacy in over a year. And Emmitt, catching on, texting me out of the blue one day: *Why're you using me and Easton put together to make one boyfriend? You fuck Easton and make me go salsa dancing. Why'd I get the bad part?*

*

Early July, 2018.

At home, my phone buzzed: Easton.

Bring a bag.

for what?

No questions Megan.

I searched "bring a bag slang," clicking on an unhelpful Urban Dictionary entry as I walked upstairs to grab a box of Häagen-Dazs bars from the freezer. Another buzz: Come over. I'd put the bars in a Lululemon bag and hoped the bag was big enough.

When I got to Easton's, the boys were sitting on the L-shaped couch in his living room, on opposite ends from one another. I held up the bag, "How's this?"

Easton looked up and said with more humor in his voice than I'd heard in weeks: "You actually brought a bag?"

"....yeah?"

He shook his head. "I was kidding, Megan."

Embarrassment rushed to my face. *Was this some sort of bet between them? To see if I'd do whatever Easton said, no questions asked?* I faltered for only a moment before resigning myself to their bizarre games that I often found myself in the middle of, throwing an ice cream bar towards Emmitt, which he caught gracefully, and putting the rest in the freezer.

Emmitt, whose socked big toe was visible through the ripped toe cap of his Vans, hardly looked up from his phone when he said, "I wanna massage."

I suppose his desire could have been directed at Easton, but I highly doubted it.

"I don't know how to give massages," I responded.

I was always answering like this with him, finding the line between being polite and declining. Once, when Emmitt had picked me up and listened to me talk about why I was still thinking about last summer with Easton, I opened up to him about my anxieties surrounding sex, to which he responded, "I could teach you if you wanted."

"You don't know how to give massages? Prolly because of your small ass hands."

Emmitt scooted over on the couch, taking no mind to what I'd just said, and waited for my hands to reach for his back.

From the far end of the couch, Easton said, "Do *you* want a massage?"

"Sure," I answered. But I was cautious. *Was it another joke?*

Easton got up and took a seat behind me. All three of us were now in a line on the couch. Only once Easton's cool fingers found their way to my shoulders did I make contact with Emmitt's t-shirt.

As I did, Emmitt snorted. "Is this a fucking massage train?"

I laughed, but was in the process of siphoning off any sensation in the hands on Emmitt's back to the parts of my body Easton was touching.

And his hands were everywhere. My shoulder blades. My neck. My waist. His thumbs reached under my tank top. Four fingers slipped under the waistband of my denim shorts. He traced small circles against my ribcage, rubbing rib by rib, making his way up, higher and higher till he was at the top. And then I felt his teeth, sharp on my shoulder, exhaling silently so that only he and I knew. And then he got up, walked into the kitchen, turned on the kitchen faucet and filled a glass with water.

I dropped my hands from Emmitt's back, and sat in a daze, wanting to stretch out every moment of Easton's massage till it was like taffy between my teeth. The taste sweet on my tongue.

The three of us went out to a kava bar in Berkeley: the two of them sipping the bitter liquid served in bowls and me sucking on the cherries that accompanied their order. I'd pet the dog in the bar, we'd look at the picture books on the shelf, I'd say I was cold and Easton would gaze down at my white tank top, say "I can tell," and when the night got dark, Emmitt would drive us back to Easton's. As I was opening the car door, I realized out loud that I'd left my cardigan in Easton's house.

"It's a trap," Emmitt said immediately.

What light we had on Easton's street was dim. A subdued warmth radiated from the windows of the houses around us and the orange from street lamps above streamed into the car, onto our faces.

Neither Easton nor I responded.

Instead, Easton said goodbye to Emmitt and walked silently with me to his front door. The lights in his living room were off and he didn't bother turning them on. I made for my cardigan, sitting in a pile on the coffee table. When I turned around to say goodnight, I saw Easton sitting against the piano cover, his long legs rooted to the carpet below. We basked in silence and quiet. In eyes meeting eyes in the dark. He made room for me to fit between his legs, and I made my way to that space, melting into him happily. We stood there too long, in the dark of his parent's house, in each other's arms, and something inside my head warned that I should leave before it became something more.

But I wanted it to become something more. I wanted last summer's confessions and closeness.

But I'd learned by then that every time it became something more, he became distant with me again.

We'd reach for each other's bodies, we'd fall into sheets together, he'd kiss my legs, and I'd lie against the mattress, closing my eyes, wondering if I was acting correctly, wondering how I looked under his body and bent over the edge of the bed, worried about how I sounded, becoming quieter and quieter until I was fully inhabiting my head, not my body, gone from that space, gone from that bed, being turned over when he turned me over, anxiously waiting for it to be over, for him to finish and for me to enjoy the ease and openness that then radiated from him, eager for the words he'd say to me, the way he'd pucker his lips afterwards and let me kiss him slowly, the secrets of his soul waiting to be nurtured by my small hands.

And then he'd stop texting me back, tell me we weren't on the same page, sexually, and I'd be left thinking that all the things I was insecure about were probably true.

I should leave, I thought.

And I left.

*

Late July, 2018.

The three of us were eating pizza at the dining room table and listening to Prince's "It's Gonna Be So Lonely." The two of them gulped down Coronas while I gulped down water. I asked Easton, our resident artist, if he'd draw the Led Zeppelin symbols where I wanted them tattooed, on my ribcage.

"You have to dive in," Easton said. "Stop being so safe."

But that night, after telling me no, after telling me to "dive in," he drew them on me anyway — our deal being that he would draw the symbols where I wanted if he could also tag my ass. I agreed all too willingly and changed into a bikini top so he could sharpie the symbols onto my skin. Emmitt was there, too, of course, lying on the other end of the couch, scrolling through his phone while I lay down and Easton held one hand to my hip, and one against my ribcage.

Fingers dragging as he drew.

"Okay," he said. I got up to look at them in the bathroom mirror. The temporary tattoo, clumsily drawn because he'd been drinking, was a lot bigger than I expected.

"Let me see," Easton said from the living room.

I stared at myself in the mirror: bikini top and spandex, bulky sharpie lines wrapping around my ribs. There was no way in hell that I was going to parade around the living room like that for them. I scampered back to the couch, rolled onto my stomach, and finally responded: "No."

"Are you serious, Megan?" Easton said.

I got ready to roll my eyes.

"I've been inside you."

I opened my mouth.

"Sorry," he said, fingering the sharpie cap. "That probably made things worse."

Emmitt started cackling from the other end of the couch, shaking his head. At the same time, my phone started buzzing: my brother. I picked up, and as we chatted on the phone, Easton's hands and that sharpie found their way back to my body.

He covered my entire back in thick strokes of permanent marker, drawing a bonsai tree with a sun peaking out from behind its branches and two faces in profile. His signature, his tag. The kind of faces he paints on buildings around the Bay, the ones done in color on harbor walls. They're goblin-like; anti-human in appearance. Sometimes, they're painted drowning. Other times, bleeding. They're painted being eaten alive by crows, bow and arrow to the eyes. Eyeballs gone from sockets, flowers filling their place. They're painted praying in the rain. Bent over, head bowed, body aching.

When Easton was done, and I was off the phone, he took a photo of my back: no longer bare, and his hand, hiking up spandex, revealing the face he'd drawn on the whitest part of my body.

And Emmitt was on the couch, commenting that he wished he had someone he could draw on.

*

August, 2018.

At the end of the summer, Emmitt told me Easton had gotten a DUI. I didn't want to let on that I'd heard from someone other than Easton himself, but I wanted to reach out. I texted that I hadn't seen him in a while and I hoped he was doing well. Said I was there to talk, if he ever wanted.

He told me I was wasting my time.

Asked me to not text him for a while, *please.*

Ended our conversation with a peace sign emoji followed by: "bye."

I'd walk around the house I was living in at the time, at the tippy top of Panoramic Way, which sat amongst redwoods and eucalyptus and oaks. I'd watch the orange and blue sunset over the Bay, the lights on the bridge beginning to gleam. I'd put a playlist together, call it "your sadness rubbed off on me" like a simp, and fill it with the Pink Floyd and Led Zeppelin songs that made me think of him. And then I'd look through my photos from that summer, the one of my back covered in black sharpie, marked up by his hand, his drawings, mystified by the touch of Easton's hand on my body. How someone could be so entrenched in your daily life one moment, so seemingly close, and then want you out of it the next.

When I studied his paintings, the ones done on buildings all over the Bay, I'd wonder whether they were self-portraits of a sort. Pulling to the surface what took place on the interior. Calling back to the secrets he'd shared with me between sheets the summer prior. The way he'd guided our conversation into the landscapes of our minds, landscapes that felt as though they were traveling to meet each other; sand dunes stretching on and on till we found the other's outlook.

But that was how I'd felt.

He'd felt alone in his mind. He told me that. That we could be as close as physically possible — skin against skin, my body a canvas for his sketches — and still be alone in our minds.

How to lose a name
by Sharon Coleman
        according to Creation with Astral Rays *by Remedios Varo*

Fasten on long grey wings.
Keep them folded along your spine.
Eye to the narrow end of a spyglass.
Magnify hungry pollen of an otherwise placid flower inside your eye.
Scan pink residue of the last traces of water over sandbanks.
Speak the name once and note where it ricochets against canyons of flesh.
Let it echo up the grey maze as it has so often.
Let it drip from your honeyed saliva into a vial filled with astral liquid.
Look—liquid greys.
Straighten your stiff wings when you see his smoke-stained teeth again
when his dusty couch itches your thigh.
when the name comes between his crashing fist and you.
Eyes open said the abortionist in her meticulous accent.
She left something.
Take hold of the metal handle at the vial's exit tube.
Turn it to stop the knocking in plumbing between thoughts.
Water hothouse seedlings with the distilled rays.
Fan them slightly with your wings.
Release bees by the seedlings as their myriad names leaf out.
Snatches of syllables left in your throat liquefy and fade.

Admission
by Leora Fridman

I get monthly ultrasounds these days to track what's happening with my body,
the cysts that won't stop growing on my tubes. So far there aren't any answers.

Each time I go in I crane around on the crinkly paper sheet to watch the screen,
even though they tell you not to do that because you won't know what it means.
I stare at the gray triangles on the screen as they fill with empty clouds. Every
time I think only, *there's no baby in there.* Though we aren't looking for a baby.
Even my doctor doesn't know what we are looking for exactly.

But I go in anyway: I submit again to the cold lube on the big plastic wand that
goes up me. I stare at the screen and wait for some perfect sharded star that I can
blame for where it hurts.

                                        *

In *Gravity and Grace,* Simone Weil writes: "It is impossible to forgive whoever has
done us harm if we believe that harm has lowered us. We have to think that it has
not lowered us, but has revealed to us our true level."

The cyst and its burstings have done me harm. They have lowered me so many
days onto the bathroom floor where I writhe and try desperately to shit. I wait

for revelation. I want a diagnosis so that I can feel my true level of illness has been revealed to me, that these days of pain amount to something. If that, then this will be somehow useful. Maybe this is capitalism living in me, wanting each action or moment in my life to somehow be useful on a market, traded in for something of use: not a useless sack of lost days or bloated belly pain. The story to resolve itself, the moments to resolve themselves, me having been lowered to that tile floor for a reason.

But also, I'm beginning to get used to being lowered. I'm used to the routine of the few days a month I can't do anything but clutch myself as my belly blares out.

*

Recently I reached out to someone who I dated briefly when I was in college. I treated him like shit back then — was careless with his feelings, lied about what I wanted from him. Not a normal way I do things, and one that sticks with me. Generally I'm pretty nice to people, but the way I treated Alex nags at me more than eleven years later.

From the internet I find out he lives in the same city as me, frequents some of the same bars, and from then it is only a matter of time. Soon a friend tells me she ran into him, that he mentioned he knew me, and a moment of fear flashes through me.

Did he say he hates me? I laugh tightly.

Why would he? She asks. When I tell her the whole story, how I started dating someone else without telling him, how I laughed high and loud and blinked away his feelings when he stood caved over at the door to my room, she suggests I apologize, even this late.

Imagine you're in a 12-step program making amends, she tells me, *sounds like you need to clear that slate.*

It takes a few obsessive drafts, but I write him an email. In it I apologize, and I mean it. I feel remorse in the sense that I wouldn't do today what I did then, and wish my younger self had known better. Though I can't help but remind him in my email that I was young, then, after all, hadn't learned much yet, that perhaps he doesn't remember what I did, that it may not even have mattered to him.

(But he has very expressive eyes: his most marked characteristic. I knew it mattered to him, even so long ago when I got into a different car outside our apartment building and glanced back through the thick desert wind.)

*

Lately my husband and I joke about how we're both sexually submissive, and wonder whether that's a mismatch. We say maybe we will find a dom for us both. We both desire to be guided, pummeled and pegged to feel our anxious minds drop away in the bare reason of sex.

Chris Kraus on Simone Weil: "She wants to lose herself in order to be larger than herself. A rhapsody of longing overtakes her. She wants to really see."

See: I wait for the crush of pain that will lower me again this month, the plans I will have to cancel, the sick version of me who I will become.

Or, see: I write the apology email to Alex and await a response, visualizing his reply like an axe falling on my house. I daydream that he will tell all my friends what a bad person I am, that any efforts I've made toward nonviolent communication will seem like bullshit. I imagine that everyone I know will turn against me in disgust. Quickly, in this daydream, I become an evil, shunned outcast. Everyone hears about an ugly part of me and everything else I've lived up until now crushes easily — I drop out of the bottom of the dream life I've been living, and lose all semblance of a cared-for life — no friends, no family, no food, no home. In a few moments of thinking this through, I'm lying alone on the sidewalk, sunburnt and sick. The story speeds wildly away from everything I understand to mean wellness.

*

In Sick Woman Theory, Johanna Hedva writes,

"Sickness" as we speak of it today is a capitalist construct, as is its perceived binary opposite, "wellness." The "well" person is the person well enough to go to work. The "sick" person is the one who can't. What is so destructive about conceiving of wellness as the default, as the standard mode of existence, is that it *invents illness as temporary*. When being sick is an abhorrence to the norm, *it allows us to conceive of care and support in the same way*.

Care, in this configuration, is only required sometimes. When sickness is temporary, care is not normal.

The daydream is speedy, but not irrational. I've learned over years to enact my will — forcefully, with all my might — toward not being ill, toward not being rejected. As the pinpoints of sickness have increased in my life, I require more care, and the possibility of rejection from work (life, work-life) begins to seem terrifyingly close, just over the next cliff. I stay here only if my will works well enough to keep me well.

The binary deepens. I clean around my belly at a work meeting and try not to vomit. Later I get another ultrasound, and am the opposite of will: I submit. I know nothing, but I get in the stirrups again. I admit myself to the hospital again. I admit that I don't know what's happening to this body, haven't been able to keep it in line. Hoping that admitting will make the pain go.

*

Weil again: "It is impossible to forgive whoever has done us harm if we believe that harm has lowered us."

64

I was careful in my apology email not to make Alex feel lowered — didn't want to imply that he'd been reduced by the careless way I'd treated him back then.

I bet you probably didn't even notice, I write, though I know this isn't true. I want to place him as blankly powerful, unaffected by my gross, human relational mistakes, priestly now in his moral capacity to absolve my sins. If I keep him high and don't lower him, maybe then he can forgive. I keep him high and perfect in my memory, looking down at me from the tiny square windows of the Brutalist concrete dorms where we lived in Be'ersheva in 2005.

But also, I like being down there in my memory, looking up at a window at Alex's righteous face. I realize as I write the email that I am enjoying the grovelling. It feels soft. I grow pliable as I admit that I didn't act as I would have liked to, wasn't in control of myself back then, that I was sick and wretched, that I am sorry and deserve to be plied, changed, fixed by someone else.

I admit. The admission requires help, invites relationship.

*

When we meet up for drinks I see Alex across the bar before he sees me — one last moment of control before I humble myself before him. In response to the email he has agreed to meet me after work. He is dressed for an office and looks dignified. He sits high on a stool in the early-summer Oakland sun. I watch him for a moment from a corner of the bar, and picture myself briefly entering church to be absolved of my sins. I get a small thrill. I wonder what I will have to do (be *forced* to do) to gain his forgiveness. Will he give me an assignment, four days of fasting, Hail Marys before bed?

I dip into the bathroom to mess my hair, and approach his end of the bar properly frizzy, sweaty from my bike ride, and penitent. But he smiles right away. We hug and he accepts my apology within just a few minutes.

Of course I forgive you, he says, and smooths a wet napkin. *I haven't had hard feelings in years*, he says, and, *neither of us knew better*. He moves on, asks me about my new book, what he calls my *great, weird life*. He asks about my husband and I say quickly that my husband knows I'm here, that I am not trespassing in that sense. That my husband and I tell each other everything about fleeting crushes and past partners.

And you're fine with that? He asks. *I love it*, I say. I tell him I love hearing about my husband's attraction to the woman who cuts his hair, his fantasies about the people who pass him on the bike path on his way to work.

I get that, Alex tells me, *I love hearing those, too*. It turns out that he is in an open marriage, that just last month he found himself talking his wife through a heartbreak when her other lover broke up with her.

It was wild at first, but now it's starting to feel normal. Just a different kind of normal shape of marriage, he tells me, and we laugh in the soft summer light about how no one back home would think any of this was normal. But here, in the Bay Area, it is nothing special.

We both glance up at the Warriors game, and Alex asks how my family is doing. It's comfortable and easy, suddenly, to answer, to be finishing our beers together, reminiscing. But something in me feels let down. The fog-breaking ease of his forgiveness, the normalcy of it — it leaves me feeling minorly robbed. I'd liked presenting myself as guiltily soft, loose raw material that needed fixing.

(Dare I say *spanking?* Dare I say *punishment?* Dare I say *straightening out?* I face Alex and smile, but hunch on the bar stool, one last attempt to make myself small, though I am strong enough to sit up straight.)

"Like bones before they are bones," writes Bhanu Kapil, "Like eyes in the time that follows talking." Alex and I catch up like regular old friends, but when we hug goodbye I long for the anger I saw once in his huge eyes, the kinds of eyes that my Yiddish scholar friend once called *shtetl eyes,* after that sunken expressiveness, the eyes that look always older than the person they stare from, the kind of eyes that carry generations of grief.

*

I know nothing about Catholicism, but *Christianity for Dummies* tells me that, "Just as tumors are benign or malignant, Catholics believe that sins are venial or mortal." The venial ones can be absolved through penance. "Your penance is for your benefit — to remind you that God comes first and you come last," I read.

I like the order here, the stage directions: Alex and I two dark curly-haired Jews who met in Israel/Palestine, now on the West Coast playing priest and sinner in my head. But he refuses the role I assigned him, doesn't show up for our rehearsal. I don't know, then, how to resolve the story, find my proper place in line.

*

You search long enough for a diagnosis and you'll eventually find something. Once my doctor says that I likely have endometriosis, I start asking people who I know have it. Arisa tells me that if you have it they can do laparoscopic surgery (she fingers her belly where it was done on her) to remove tissue, internal scarring, and cysts.

But that doesn't solve the pain totally, she says, *unless you want to be on hormones for the rest of your life.* That's what doctors recommend, she tells me, hormones that will put you in a perimenopausal state for the foreseeable future so that no more endometrial tissue will grow. She doesn't want those hormones, Arisa tells me, so she mostly just does what she calls *pain management.*

I keep a low profile and don't ask the doctors for much, she tells me, *since I'm not doing what they say I should.* She looks up at me from under her lashes, demure, maybe even a *bad girl.*

Then she laughs and sits back, practical. She sips her iced rooibos tea. (She tells me caffeine is out entirely.) She tells me she changes her diet when she needs to, does acupuncture and massage and smokes weed when the pain pounds too intensely for her to sleep.

I just give into the pain when it's at its worst, she tells me, *after a while I learned to look forward to it.* She tells me her pain brings a time of the month of altered states and possibility. She tells me she wrote all of her last book while in one long swoop of pain.

Being roughed down by the pain is generative for her. Or, she finds her own way to top it.

I write, I walk, Arisa tells me, *I ride the pain instead of collapsing.*

*

When I have a flare-up while my parents are visiting, my friends nod sagely and remind me how we all regress around our families.

Of course you had it then, sweetheart, Jo texts me, *the little girl inside you wants to let go.*

I feel resistant about this, though — I think because it implies I have some agency I don't feel — or don't want — in how and when I get sick. (If I got sick when my parents were here, does that make it my fault?)

My doctor has another thought about the parent flare-up. She says stress exacerbates my symptoms. Again, pain is something I cause upon myself. Do I intentionally lower myself at the feet of that porcelain throne and throw up while my mom is on her way over for breakfast? My body-will sweeps through me, and I am on the floor again.

*

In a more awake moment I tell my husband about the emails with Alex. My husband is proud of me, excited for me, commends me on my *courageous adult communication skills.*

You're an emotional adventurer, he smiles, *and I love how you plumb these depths.* I feel myself begin to glow with specialness, oceanic and deep.

Wayne Koestenbaum writes: "I may be humiliated, but because I am seen in the process of exhibiting my shame, I therefore gain *the pleasure of exemplarity*." I am special in my humility, in my morning pain and my amends.

I'm impressed, my husband says, *with how willing you are to make yourself vulnerable.* He wraps his big body around me on the couch and I shiver.

Willing? I say, *I don't know if I will it.* I feel more bendy than will. Riding the pain is more a relaxing of will than a decision. I ready myself, slow my work pace, cut all spices from my diet, have to cancel plans. I tuck my will into bed.

Here I am lying on tile again, waiting for my husband to rush home and take me to the ER. My body jerks from the middle outward and the moan isn't mine, just a groaning voice that inhabits me as I focus on continuing to breathe. I think of nothing but when the next jerk will come, like how my mom-friends describe contractions when they were giving birth. (We breathe. We know it will pass.) I ride one wave of pain and wait for the next. I sweet-talk myself, *yes, baby girl, you're going to be fine*, I croon in a whisper, *this will be over soon*.

And it is. By the time my husband gets home the pain is over for today, and there is nothing to do but recover and rest. My body is still jelly so we lie there for a while, him stroking back my hair like I would never let him do any other time.

Just relax, my sweet baby, he says, *oh, my baby*. Because there is no other word.

Smell the Moxie
by Heather June Gibbons

My project is plain persistence, self as spatula
scraping self as burned crud off skillet, pretend
research in a field of forget-me-nots sprayed
with real pesticides, grief that never gets past

bargaining, the whole *what if* and *if only*,
elaborate mazes out of wet cardboard, a little
cologne for the armpits, we're talking real
Band-Aid solutions here, a jerry-rigged screen

door on a sagging front porch where a man
with a shotgun across his knees is sleeping,
an outboard motor that starts up about every
umpteenth yank, but only when you choke it.

I have this habit of breaking keys off in locks,
drawer knobs come off in my hands, slobber
dries on my thighs, when I say *doing okay*
I mean an ongoing white-knuckling, when I ask

how you are, I hear furnace, then praxis, think
wax, expats, and other kinds of justice, tell you
can't, have to walk my hair and wash the dog,
key my own car then drive it through a wall.

Pennies over my eyes and still this throb
in my trousers. Not a pretty place. Left
to my own devices, I play until they break.
I keep turning this roll of invisible tape

hoping to catch an edge I can peel from.
Who wants to see my discursive knees?
Cordon the fire lane, adjust the thermostat,
squeeze out the very last dab of paste.

When I say *take a stab*, I mean get a grip,
meaning grasp, meaning straws.

Buoyancy
by Jamey Gallagher

While Harold was in the process of dying, Marion's life was swallowed up in that dying. She had no life of her own. But that was the way it was supposed to be. If things had been reversed, Harold would have given his life up for her and gone swirling down the drain of unending appointments: tests and treatments. He would have been the late night caregiver, holding her or just sitting up with her, allowing her to vent, cleaning up her bodily fluids, dealing with her smell. It was just a matter of chance that it was him who got sick, not her.

Still, she was unbearably relieved when, after seven years, Harold finally died. Seven years was a long time to put a life on hold, but Marion had. She had left her job as a paralegal, and they had survived on savings and on Harold's pension from the Army. She would never tell anyone how she felt on the morning that he died, in the twin bed they had moved out of the guest room into the living room. It was so early in the morning the nurse they'd hired to come in had not arrived yet. Wearing yellow pants and a white blouse, Marion was sitting up in bed with him, gazing out the window at the front yard, obscured by a crawling fog. She was lazily running her hand through the tufts of hair that had grown back on his head. By that point he was no longer Harold at all. He had not been Harold for a long time. She heard the death rattle in the back of his throat and could feel him— his spirit? his soul?— jar out of his body and... waft away. She would cry later. She would mourn the lost Harold she hadn't started mourning yet, but when she felt him leave she smiled. She actually smiled. She closed her eyes, smiled, and breathed deeply, knowing that it was finally over.

She went into their bedroom— *her* bedroom now— and changed out of the pants and the shirt and into a yellow one-piece swimsuit. She looked at herself in the mirror above the dresser. Fifty one years old, she barely recognized herself. Her hair was short, helmet-shaped, and swept to the side, her shoulders were rounded, her skin was pale.

Outside, the fog was lifting. It was chilly. The water in the in-ground pool was warmer than the air. She swam slowly from one end of the pool to the other, back and forth, wishing she had a larger pool. Often she had felt trapped here, the pool her only recourse, a way to hold her energy steady, but now she felt like she could escape. She imagined the pool extending for miles, imagined swimming for miles. She felt buoyant.

When the nurse arrived and told Marion that Harold had passed, she cried. It was not for show. Once they started, the tears were authentic. But she would never forget the smile that had crept across her face when she first realized he was gone. Sometimes she suspected she was the worst person in the world— despite the fact that so many people were obviously far worse. At least they were horrible in the open. She was secretly corrupt.

*

She called Harold's twin brother, Tom, who said he would drive over to help. She had friends in the neighborhood, but she had drifted away from them in the last seven years and didn't feel like she knew them well enough to ask for help. Many of them were younger than her, raising children. They watched their tots ride big wheels and jump on inchworms in their driveways, and after a while Marion had felt too separate from the young mothers and stopped sitting out with them.

Tom arrived, with an air of purpose. Marion had always been disquieted by Tom. Though he and Harold were identical twins, their experiences had changed them enough so that no one would ever mistake one for the other. Tom was the gruffer, more confident brother. He had a straighter back and broader shoulders. He took things in hand, calling family and friends, flipping through her rolodex on the kitchen table, the yellow phone receiver in his fist. It was as if Harold were not dead but had turned into a stronger, more confident man. She had always appreciated the softness of Harold, at least at first. Now she was relieved by Tom's strength.

She sat in the front room with the dead body until men from the funeral home arrived. The body exuded something. It was already disintegrating. They had made arrangements ahead of time: a wake, a burial plot in the cemetery a few miles away, just outside the small downtown, where she could visit whenever she wanted to. The two men from the funeral home came bearing a stretcher with wheels. Tom stood watching with his shoulder against the doorframe.

When the men and her husband's body were gone, she felt alone but also surveilled. Tom was watching her.

"I'm so sorry, Marion," he said, hugging her. She recognized the feel of her husband's body in the body of this man she barely knew. Both brothers had served in the war. Tom had been in the Navy, while Harold had been stationed stateside with the Army. He'd given tours of the USS Constitution in Massachusetts while Tom had killed men in Togo. His body was like Harold's body, with broader shoulders and the stomach bloused out. There were ginflowers on his nose and cheek. She could smell his slightly rancid breath.

She didn't realize at first what was happening. She simply wondered why Tom didn't break the hug, why he clung to her. But then she realized that he was crying, his shoulderblades rising and falling. And then he was sobbing, and it was her who was comforting him.

*

She felt lost, unable to find her way through all the time suddenly available to her. She woke before dawn listening for Harold in the living room, ready to get up and bring him a drink of water, ready to rub his back if he choked or coughed. Then she would remember that he was gone.

Every morning she swam in the pool, but after a while the pool was too small. She started going to the Y in the morning and using the Olympic size pool. She worked on the form of strokes she had almost forgotten over the years. The butterfly stroke. The breast stroke. There were a half dozen women like her, middle-aged, presumably alone, swimmers. They avoided each other, usually, or

70

made halfhearted greetings in the locker room, their wet feet splayed on the tiles, their bathing caps lending them anonymity.

She felt her body changing because of the swimming, her shoulders becoming stronger, her stomach slimmer.

*

At home she found it difficult to read or to watch her programs or to clean or to cook or to do anything, really. Tom had helped her move the twin bed back into the guest room and the marks from the bed's legs were still imprinted in the living room carpet. She listened to music, without words. Soft jazz and, more and more often, classical music. Debussy, Chopin and Beethoven's sonatas. She didn't care what she was supposed to like, what was considered "great." She liked slow, moody, atmospheric pieces. She liked piano. She liked the spaces between notes.

She would sit in the living room drinking a glass of bourbon and listening to music while the light failed, not bothering to turn on the lamps. She would take long showers at seven or eight at night, hot showers that left her skin wrinkled. She got a new job as a paralegal and she did the work thoroughly and thoughtfully.

*

She didn't say no when Tom offered to come to the house and make her dinner. Squid ink pasta with shrimp and lots of garlic. Something he had learned to make during the war, he told her. From a woman he had been seeing. She assumed that "woman" probably meant "prostitute" in that scenario, but it was no business of hers.

She remembered Tom at the burial, several months before, devastated by the loss of his brother. She had never seen him, or any other man, cry so much. He must have felt like a piece of himself, the better piece, had died. He must have regretted.

They didn't talk about Harold. Instead, Tom talked about his experiences, stories she had never heard before. He had almost been married three times, he told her. He had a son from one of those women, a grown son who was living in Santa Fe. She'd had no idea. He showed her pictures and shrugged. When she looked at his face it was hard not to see Harold's face. When he left that night he held on to the small of her back as he hugged her, and she felt something that she wanted to deny but couldn't.

*

The first time they made love she felt her heart dissolving, rising to the surface of her skin, then spreading out. It was a delicious kind of shame. It felt incestous, almost, but of course it wasn't. His brother had seen her, had known her whole body, but he had never touched her like Tom did.

When it was over, she felt as if she had just made love with a ghost. He breathed above her, her head on his chest. She fit exactly the way she had with Harold. But Harold had slowly wasted away over seven years so that there was no resting her head against his chest toward the end. He had curled up inside himself and disappeared.

"That was wrong," she said.

He grunted and shrugged. He put on his short-sleeved shirt and his chinos and went outside to smoke by the pool. She put on a robe and joined him, and she felt like she was in a strange movie from the 1940s, a movie that hadn't mastered the tropes of mystery and psychological darkness yet, back when symbols could mean almost anything. The mosquitos bit at them.

*

No one from his family came to the wedding. They all thought the marriage was wrong, strange, unholy. Over the years— there were many years of robust and mutually satisfying sex, followed by mellower years where they made love once or twice a week, sometimes successfully, always comfortably— her old husband's body would be subsumed within her new husband's. He was both soft and hard. He cried in a way Harold had never cried, at movies and commercials and the sad events that accompany any life.

Sometimes she would see Harold looking out of Tom's eyes, and she would smile, remembering when he passed.

It was just a temporary relief, she wanted to tell him. A fleeting buoyancy.

After
by Elizabeth Riley

1.
As it got dark
On the day of resurrection
I boarded my flight
Companioned by all that remained
A plastic rectangular box
Properly labeled
Inspected under florescent lights
By agents looking for bombs
Only to find a dead father
Ashes are only substantial
When compact
Tossed on the surface
Of clear water
Drifting apart
The space between particles aching
With absence and abrasive light

All the Beautiful Things This Kitchen Held
by Kehinde Badiru

That night, I knew he loved my body and not my soul, one Friday evening in August, when we were in the kitchen. As usual, he told me how much he misses us; the time we spent together, and how I've become distant from him. I had just prepared dinner, and evening was closing in on itself. Outside was calm. He stretched himself closer to me, nearing one of the kitchen cabinets, "How do you feel inside of you?" He whispered, holding me from behind.

"I don't know," I said with a voice that matched his whisper — the kind of one you make when you are about to tell a lie.

I looked at him with a resigned expression. My sister, Ivie was in the living room phoning her friend, Joyce, whom I had dated for three years before we went our separate ways last Easter. The day we met, it felt as if I had never loved anyone, "that will hurt your teeth" I said to her while she reached for the new cracker biscuit, a new product at *Bath and Loud* supermarket, off Adeniyi Jones Avenue, Ikeja, Lagos. That was our favorite place to shop as a family and was also my mum's. That night, Joyce went for something else, a terse cake-biscuit which we both shared. I had tasted the new cracker biscuit the last time I visited the supermarket. It was hard and the taste was as bland as the packaging. She didn't have it, and I discouraged her from tasting it. We smiled that night crunching our terse cake-biscuit with her favorite yogurt. But our love didn't last long as the taste of her favorite yogurt.

"I'm sorry, I don't feel too well"

"What?"

"You asked me how I felt inside of me."

"Yes," He had stopped holding me from behind. His eyes journeyed from the frying pan to my hands as I fried plantain to go along with rice and stew.

"You had asked. I wasn't listening. I'm sorry," I said.

His eyes were heavy, movement rapid from earlier drunkenness. They watched my own eyes carefully. This was how he lost his wife, pretending to be happy. Because he is sad, you can't understand what his eyes want, what message they are passing across. Only alcohol understands. This Kitchen holds every memory he has of my Mother: where they had their tiny quarrels over what school we would attend when we first moved here in 2012, where he made hot love to Mother, the product, a male child which didn't live more than 4 weeks after birth. My grandma said that child wasn't supposed to live after all, that God wanted him home as quickly as possible, in preparation for her death. Grandma would often say she couldn't wait to join the baby in heaven. She was obsessed with this child as though she knew how heaven was being run or she was God's assistant. She rehearsed her death several times, in preparation for how she would be welcomed by this boy who never got to live. But the more she prepared for death, the livelier she became, the longer she lived. My Mother never left the kitchen even when it wasn't time to cook; she loved the place and all the songs the white walls inspire. On these walls and in the utensils are grandma's homage to this child that never lived. The death of this baby, who was supposed to be our last born broke Mama. She became distant, divided, delusional, distracted from life. She found a new life in the kitchen. Grandma would often nag at her daughter's absentmindedness and her indecision to move on — when in fact she had every reason to move on, in that she had two children already who she believed *Osanobua*, will keep safe. Grandma's words fell off from the right ear after entering through the left. My Mother left.

My father's innocence died the night our Mother left him for his best friend. Something else in him died too. Something in us died, with all the love we had for her. What makes a mother leave her children and husband for another man, a stranger? It's something no one will understand, not a good thing to write about or even tell your friends who had created El Dorado-dreams of what marriage is. She was broken and tired of her marriage with my dad. The happiness she sought was not present in our family. She would come home every night from her lover's house with a different kind of face, a different kind of souvenir, weeks before she left. We hadn't known that each new souvenir held the love that will be lost, to be found somewhere else. But I expected her to stay, to wait, to remember all the beautiful things this kitchen held. It was wide, L-shaped and the most experimental kitchen any family living in metropolitan Lagos could wish for. Ivie had drafted the design of the kitchen she thought would be best for the family. We marveled at how exactly she fulfills the meaning of her name — precious ornament. Being a baking enthusiast, she wanted more space for her and Mama where they could experiment whilst cooking and baking, and create precious moments. The Kitchen housed brown painted cabinets, with two rows and a column of glasses dividing them. In between the opposite cabinets is a center-carved-table made of wood that held tiny kitchen utensils. Its legs were long, about four feet, and V-shaped in that of the elbow of an old sage. This was the history behind this special table. Mama came to love this particular table. She said it was her personal space — all the beautiful dishes she ever prepared started on this table, all the worries she'd have, the solace she'd ever need. The table was one of Grandma's gifts to her when we were moving into this new house. She said modernity had replaced the life she knew and this specially sculpted wooden table would remind her grandchildren that we came from a village where the fine woodcarvers in Nigeria are from.

*

"Esosa" Ivie called out from the living room. We didn't hear her words from the kitchen at first; the TV set was too loud. Had she forgotten to reduce the volume so she could hear us? She called me for a second time.

Outside was dark already; the kitchen was too. He was seated on the center-carved-table, "It's breaking me. I don't understand," he said.

"Dad, you have to be better," I said, tired of his nag and utter disappointment.

He stood up, almost losing balance, "How do I cope without your love? Esosa" he whined, his eyes still moving rapidly.

I should have noticed how my dad had loved me, carefully after my Mother left him. He had never felt more intimate than when their marriage was stable. He kissed me once when we were alone, and then more kisses. He said I was everything his youth wasn't, and he hoped to fix this by loving me the right way. I wonder what tenderness he felt from my lips, one that he couldn't get anywhere else. As long as it reminded him of his tenderness, greater than what he had ever known, I was ready to be the reason he smiles. But I wonder what he saw in me.

74

"Do you ever ask me what I want?" I asked him, setting out the dinner plates.

"I wouldn't know since you became distant," he defended with a teary eye. "You have all you'd ever need," he added, fingering the edge of the wooden table, perhaps to contain how he felt.

If God could see how I felt inside, he'd see that this man's love was supposed to be my soul.

"Dad…" I hadn't finished what I wanted to say. I wanted to tell him that he drives me crazy, and makes loving easy. He stretched himself closer to me, touching my ears, cradling my eyes.

"What's going on here?" It was Ivie's voice. At that moment my life began to redefine God's gift to me as it is with the meaning of my name — Esosa.

Un/Body
after Die Verwandlung
by Klein Vorhees

From un/settling dreams
comes myself monstrous

waking the small yellow ditch
in my breast.
I trace it, shedding

every layer I can.
Jagged nails catching
on the puckered

edges forming a question un/bidden

what would my chest feel
if that incision had kept
going, after the tumor?
Fatty tissue un/furling
ribbons from my ribs.

I sink my fingers into that murk,
to parse shuddering geography
of the Un/geziefer.
Negated / body of skins and stings

pressing themselves into
un/godly sentences.

I see un/body skittering

myself beneath my feet
trembling inside this un/forgiving

skin desperate to un/become.

Clicking black tusks
cradle the swell of my chest,
horned tips sliding beneath
the flesh and un/shelling
                    a being
         blessedly
    un/recognizable.

I stretch my manys
thrumming the air

spindly limbs shrieking
open the shattering.

A Pandemic Year, Measured in Gray Hairs
by Molly Montgomery

My mother used to spend an hour once a week plucking the gray hairs
from her scalp, as if by removing the single strands she could unravel the fabric
of time. When it got to be too much, she started dyeing her hair light brown,
even lighter than my own hair. She dyed it brown instead of her natural black
so people would recognize her as my mother. People mistook her for my nanny
when I was a baby, since they assumed the Asian woman pushing a seemingly
white baby in a stroller was the hired help. She would correct people by saying,
"No, she's mine, I gave birth to her." Maybe she thought that by dyeing her hair
a similar shade to mine, she could pull me closer, back to the closeness we had
before I told her, at age eight, that I hated her.

My mother took me to therapy after I said this. I overheard her telling
the therapist that the final straw that prompted her to make an appointment
was when she tripped on our unevenly paved driveway and I didn't even offer
to help. I just kept walking. She thought I was lacking in empathy. I think I only
lacked empathy for her. Nothing could touch her, certainly not anything I did. So
I took her for granted.

The therapist directed me to choose a figurine from the dozens of action figures, glass figures, and doodads lining her shelf. I chose a foam swan.
I remember the sound of the crunchiness of the foam when I placed it into the
sandbox. I returned to that swan every time. I don't remember what I said during the therapy sessions. Aside from having a heightened sense of anxiety and
perfectionist tendencies as a child, I don't think there was anything that unusual
about me. I just didn't view my mother as a person yet, which is probably the
case for most eight-year-olds.

During the pandemic, my mother gave up on coloring her hair. After cutting her own hair for a few months, she decided she never needs to set foot in a hair salon again. She's embraced the gray strands, letting them colonize her head.

I was glad when I heard she wouldn't go back to the hairdresser, even wearing a mask. I wanted her to do whatever she could to reduce her risk, since she has Type II diabetes, diabetes which I feel partially responsible for since the first time she was diagnosed with it was when she was pregnant with me. I know it's irrational to view myself as the cause of her diabetes. Women with gestational diabetes are more likely to develop Type II diabetes later, but that doesn't mean one causes the other. Still, my mother never fails to remind me that diabetes made her pregnancy onerous. She had to go to the doctor to get her finger pricked most days, she had to take her maternity leave early, and she had to watch what she ate, unable to indulge in even watermelon. Without knowing, she was trying out the diet she would be tied to permanently, after her type II diagnosis.

When I ask her why she never had a second child, as she had originally planned, she gives me one of two answers: "We stopped at one because you were perfect" or "We stopped at one because I couldn't go through that again."

My grandmother's most important appointment was with her hairdresser. The lady who cut her hair was Vietnamese, which in another era, my grandmother might not have accepted. She disapproved of my uncle's high school prom date who was Japanese, and she even disliked my mother having a Filipina friend in kindergarten. In those days, my grandmother believed that people should stick to their own, not even just their own race, but their own ethnicity. But in her 90s, my grandma was more open-minded. She had a white son-in-law and a half-Chinese granddaughter. She voted for Obama, even if it was only for his second term. She liked her gossipy Vietnamese hairdresser even if she didn't understand the gossip that was in Vietnamese.

What made my grandmother want to dye her hair a deep blood red? Was it for good luck? Was it more interesting than dyeing it black or brown? I never asked. She died in 2016 at the age of ninety-three, only opening up to me about her life in her last year.

I only have one picture of my grandmother, my mother, and me together, at my eighth grade graduation. I'm wearing a magenta and white lei. There, we are, three generations, our hair auburn, tawny brown, and sepia.

While visiting my parents, I hear my mother's phone make a cheerful jingle. Each time, she stops talking with me to scroll through her phone, like a teenager checking texts.

"What app is that?" I ask her. We are sitting in the kitchen of my parents' home in the Oakland hills, which has a view of the city spread below it.

"It's the Citizen app," she tells me, informing me that every time her phone chimes, a crime has been reported somewhere nearby.

I want to roll my eyes, to point out that the app is probably feeding my mother's paranoia, but as she lists out the serious crimes that have been committed nearby — armed robberies, muggings, shootings — I don't know how to respond. I can launch into a discussion of the factors contributing to the recent rise in crime: high unemployment, economic pain, violence prevention programs in Oakland being put on hold because of the pandemic. Or I can point out that crime is much lower now in Oakland than it was when I was growing up. But I can't deny my mother's caution is warranted.

Though my mother is a senior, she is sturdy and athletic, not someone who looks like an easy target for crime. Yet I know that her race alone singles her out. The less time she spends out and about, the lower her risk for being the victim of a hate crime. It's a calculus I wish I didn't have to make, and something that never crossed my mind before the recent massacre of Asian women in Georgia and attacks on Asian elders in Chinatown. My mom, on other hand, has always been hyper-aware of the dangers lurking at every street corner, and now her fears have been vindicated.

My grandmother was also concerned about being the victim of a crime. She wouldn't answer the door unless she knew we were coming in advance, and even then, we had to bang on the door and shout at her loud enough that she recognized our voices, since she was going deaf.

What would my grandmother have done without her hair appointments, had she been alive this past year? How would she have passed her days in isolation, unable to spend half the day unhurried in the supermarket, cupping the melons to check their ripeness? Each touch would have been fraught with danger. Each moment spent inside the taxi with the windows rolled up would have been tense. She would never have left her house for fear of being a victim of a virus or an attack.

Would she have ever felt comfortable using a smartphone to video chat? I doubt she would have worn a mask, not when she worked so hard on her make-up before she went out on errands.

My grandmother lived alone during the last ten years of her life, after her husband passed away. I never asked her if she got lonely. She seemed freed by her solitude, able to do things as she liked at her own pace. When I talked to her about her past, she told me that I should not be in a rush to get married because I had so much life to experience before settling down. She didn't marry until she was twenty-nine, which was late for her generation.

She was a true child of the Depression, so maybe the scarcity of the pandemic would not have frightened her. For all the hardships she experienced, I don't think she ever saw a therapist. When she heard my parents were in therapy, she would tsk with disapproval. To her, therapy was not something Chinese people needed.

The only times I sought therapy as an adult were in grad school. It was around that time I found my first gray hair, so white that I mistook it for a blond highlight. I traced it all the way up my scalp until I found it was rooted there.

At twenty-four, they took longer to show up than they did for my mom at eighteen. But then again, as she's reminded me many times, she worked as a retail clerk at a grocery store for ten years before graduating from college, much different than the jobs I've held.

My visits to a therapist stemmed from overwhelming anxiety, first political anguish over the 2016 election, and then hypochondria that stemmed from the aftermath of an antibiotic-resistant infection. For months after I had healed from it, catastrophic thoughts rattled around my head of what would happen the next time I needed to take antibiotics: Having a relapse might mean needing to drop out of grad school. To be forced to quit my grad program for health reasons was my greatest fear, but also a fantasy I secretly indulged. I imagined sometimes how nice it would feel not having to be anywhere or do anything.

During those months, I had the nagging fear that I would never get back to "normal." When I was dealing with the infection, and in the months after, I would wake up during the middle of the night panicking, and then the next morning I would lie in bed well past my alarm, willing myself to fall back asleep because that was the only time I felt like everything was OK. At one point walking around the block was as much effort as I could muster. I used most of my energy to hide from the world what I was experiencing.

So when the pandemic hit, I had a surprising feeling of déja-vû, and the realization that my experience with illness had prepared me mentally for a year of wiping down surfaces, a year of worrying about community spread and how to prevent it, a year of lying in bed wondering every morning if I could go back to sleep and wake up in a "normal" world.

I haven't seen a therapist during the pandemic. I've been close to seeking one out a few times, but so far I've been able to use the tools I gained from my last course of therapy to cope. I suppose that's growth. Add that to the list of things that have grown during this pandemic: my coping skills and my long, brown, easily tangled hair, now sprinkled with just a pinch of silver.

I have yet to make up my mind if I want to fight the gray like my mother and my grandmother did before me. My mom has accepted that it's a battle no longer worth fighting, but my grandmother dyed her hair until the very end. I still have a few decades at least before I must worry about gray overtaking my brown. In the past year, more gray hairs have popped up, especially at my temples, but for now I still have to squint to make them out. The only solid plan I've made for after I'm fully vaccinated is to get a haircut. Not a color for now, just a cut. I can't wait for that dizzy feeling you get when you chop off a foot of hair and your head seems to float. For just a slight moment, you feel outside the rules of gravity, able to bend space-time as you please.

Weights & Measures
by Julie L. Moore

In the unpredictable calculus of their separation, he comes
& goes—she can't stop his returning to pour salt

into the softener or trim trees, as though such acts count
as some sort of penance. He owns the house, too.

So he makes himself at home, sitting at the breakfast bar,
running through receipts to throw his weights

& measures around, balancing his self-made
scales of justice in the budget.

The wife washes the dishes, her teeth
grinding, digging into her tongue,

as her husband subtracts every part of her he can,
complaining as he goes how inadequate

everything is, how nothing adds up.
She deciphers how to breathe only when he leaves.

First appeared in *Particular Scandals: A Book of Poems*; reprinted with permission by Wipf &
Stock Publishers, https://wipfandstock.com/9781620327883/particular-scandals/.

Our Love Was My Home
by Anne H. Putnam

We'd bought the land for a good price and taken a chance on building the house
ourselves, painstakingly collecting materials and learning carpentry techniques
as we went along. We knew it would be difficult, but we figured we had the time
and we enjoyed each other's company, so what did we have to lose, really? Best
case scenario: we would save thousands on rent and avoid the loneliness we'd
both felt before we found each other; worst case: we'd find new places to live,
separately, and would learn some new things along the way.

The foundation and framing were the easy part, if labor-intensive. We mixed
concrete, bought two-by-fours and nail guns, and watched hours of YouTube
tutorials. The concrete was uneven, but sound, and we thought the slanted floors
would give the place character. The walls went up, then came back down, were
re-framed, and went back up. As the sun set each evening, we lay on our backs
in what would eventually be the front yard and watched the sky darken, listened
to the deafening sound of the cicadas. He reached for me and I rolled into him,
snuggling my face into his damp shirt and squeezing his torso to keep mine from
bursting.

We had to hire professionals to wire and plumb the place – no amount of internet research could make me confident touching electric wires, and I wasn't willing to risk his life either. Money was tight, but I put in the time to gather quotes from multiple sources, and I also prostrated myself before multiple professionals, begging them for their best possible price and bribing them with baked goods. I beat egg whites and melted chocolate in a makeshift double-boiler, my anxiety infusing the treats with incantations.

It worked. We found tradesmen we could afford and I continued to ply them with pastries, keeping them sweet and assuaging my guilt. He was embarrassed by this – he felt we deserved a bit more dignity, and a lot more financial freedom – but I reassured him that I would sacrifice myself on the altar of dignity for both our sakes, and one day maybe it wouldn't be necessary anymore.

It took a year and a half of sleeping outside before the rudimentary structure was complete and weather-tight, and as soon as it was, we moved in, living in the house while we made it a home.

We spent the next four years painting and decorating, wall by wall and piece by piece. I marveled at how rarely we argued – in fact, it was frustrating sometimes to have him agree to every paint color I suggested. There was little back and forth, and mostly I just chose a color. After a period of time, he began to intuit my style, and became more comfortable bringing home furniture he thought I'd like. His personal taste seemed to change, too, leaning toward expensive, 'timeless' western European aesthetics. His brown leather round-toed 'nice shoes' were replaced with laceless ankle boots and pointy oxfords hand-hewn by generations-old shopkeepers; I didn't ask how much they'd cost, just focused on how happy they made him. If he was morphing before my eyes, it was into a handsomer, more dapper version of the man I loved. Who could complain about that?

Meanwhile, I scoured the internet for secondhand pieces and shopped the sales. I prided myself on having the magic touch for finding deals: a vintage kitchen dresser for 10% of the usual cost; a hand-painted dining table for $40 and cab fare. I discovered the thrill of the bargain, while he developed a deep attachment to the joy of spending more than he had. Still, we shared a passion for cooking, for good food and wine, for reading together in our new bed – one of the few new items of furniture we had, since he refused to sleep in a secondhand one.

As the to-do list ran down to one or two evergreen items, we settled into our home, and each other. We shared the space as if we could predict each other's movements, dancing fluidly, forever in sync. We designated a room as a nurs-ery, talked names and colors and parenting ideologies – sometimes, in the pale golden light of almost-dark, I could swear I saw the crib against the far wall, or his long, lean body in a rocker in the corner, murmuring to a little bundle in his arms.

We looked at adoptable puppies online, debating whether it would be better to have a dog before a baby, or visa versa. We checked our home value online, pleased to see it going steadily up, and talked about where we would retire if we sold the house to fund our twilight years. I pictured us in a studio apartment in Trastevere, walking out every morning to have cappuccinos at our local bar. He talked about a pied a terre in Paris, jamon-stuffed demi-baguettes by the Seine. We lay in bed together on Saturday mornings, scenes from our life to come unwinding across the ceiling like vines growing before our eyes.

It was only a couple of years before the end that I began to smell it: a sickly sweet rotting smell. Whenever I paused to sniff the air in a room, he rolled his eyes, said I was imagining it. Teased me about my super-smeller nose while he pulled me in and reminded my body of how well it fit into his.

I believed him. How could such a beautiful, still-new house have problems already? Besides, I'd helped build it – surely if there was something awry I would have noticed it earlier. I burned sage in every room – double in the nursery – and spent the next year lighting fancy scented candles and pretending I didn't feel nauseated by the smell on a daily basis. Eventually, he became frustrated by what he called my obsession. If I mentioned it, we argued, and I hated that. So I backed off, curled inward, tried to stop smelling it.

But it only got worse, and by the second summer it was so strong I couldn't ignore it anymore. He caught me on my hands and knees, nose thrust into the gap between the floor and the bottom of the door to the guest bedroom. He yanked me up, told me again that I was being crazy, that I was inventing problems, that I was trying to ruin what we'd built. I cried, my frustration at living with this undiagnosable smell – living with it *alone*, despite his constant presence – overwhelming me. He held me, shushed me, stroked my hair. You're stressed, he said. You're imagining things.

I was stressed. Our beautiful house had begun to show cracks, and I felt like every day there was something new to spackle or repair. There were strange sounds, bumps in the night, but instead of bumps they were low moans or sharp shrieks that echoed in my mind long after they'd stopped. I needed help investigating the sounds and holding the house together, but whenever I asked he just said I was hearing things, it was probably just an animal outside. Besides, he didn't have time to waste chasing down ghosts.

Then came the day I needed to replace a floorboard. I'd dropped the heavy cast-iron dutch oven the day before, narrowly missing my toe and putting a deep, ugly crack in the board it landed on. We had extra in the basement, and I knew better than to wait for his help. But when I knelt and pulled up the damaged board, the smell hit me so hard I gagged. I ran to the sink, threw up, then wrapped a tea towel around my face and went back to see what it was. I expected a rat, maybe a possum, but a human face, frozen in a rigor mortis scream, greeted me instead.

I screamed, then shut my mouth, afraid. I couldn't stop myself – I reached for the next board and yanked it up, then the next. I worked my way through the whole house until my fingers were bleeding: I found three bodies in the kitchen, four in the living room, and another two in the nursery. I was too afraid to look in our bedroom, though I knew they were there too – for months I'd felt too sick from the smell to sleep properly.

When he came home, I was huddled in the corner of the front hall, the only place where the floorboards hadn't been hiding anything. I yelped when I saw him, shrank back into myself, accused him so hard my throat closed up; he denied it over and over, even as their unseeing eyes stared up at us from their shallow graves.

I moved out, stayed with a friend. He called every hour that first day, until my friend turned my phone off and held me for a long time. He left messages, his voice husky with tears, his words full of grief at his own loss, but when I texted him back to ask if he was ready to tell me everything, he dodged and avoided and asked me how to get rid of the bodies. I threw my phone across the room.

All I wanted was to come home. For us to work on clearing out the rot and restoring the house together, from a foundation of truth. But every time I tried, I would end up fleeing in fury all over again.

Eventually, I agreed to move back in – if he moved out. He did, moving into a friend's sublet and continuing to call and text every day to tell me how much he loved and missed me. Meanwhile, I called a removal service and had the bodies taken out, piece by piece, then I scrubbed every inch of the house. Especially the bedroom, where I refused to sleep alone. Instead, I curled up in the front hall on a camping mattress, the door unlocked in case I needed to flee again. He never came by to help with clean-up, although he did stop in a couple of times to see if I was over it yet.

But I couldn't get over it. I wanted to, wanted nothing more than to go back to what we had, but I still smelled the decay. I couldn't scrub my memory clean of him, of the early days, our shared excitement and synchronous dancing, or of the lies and death I'd been living in for who knew how long.

Eventually, he stopped calling so much. I heard he moved in with someone else, a woman. Someone less sensitive, who breathed whatever air was given her and never sniffed like a bloodhound. Someone who could love him without demanding answers.

I still live in the house. I have no choice; it's my home.

-every monsoon exhausts itself eventually

By Valerie Wong

i wrote like a wildfire all night
used my words as breadcrumbs
to guide myself out of the black forest
until my hands shook
and the moon traded places with the sun
and i stumbled at last out of the labyrinth
clear-eyed and hungry for light again

Isolation

Someone
by Marilyn Abildskov

Someone writes on Twitter *I can't wait till this is over.*
Someone writes *I'm going hug every last one of you.*
Someone writes *I'm going to French kiss you all.*
Someone posts selfies, every day a different dress, always bright colors.
Someone draws a picture every day. A black cat. A kingfisher. A mole rat. A man.
Someone calls someone every morning. A sister. A mother. A neighbor. A friend.

How are you?
Did you sleep?
Did you get the masks we sent?
Did you get the soup we sent?

Someone tries to imagine what's it's like for her someone. The lethargy. The isolation. The mess of mail piling up. The dirty cat litter. Comic cobwebs

Someone counts the days since she knows her someone showered. Listens for the inhale, then exhale, after her someone takes a drag. The hours must unfold one cigarette at a time. She imagines her reaching for a bottle of wine, filling a glass. Washing the glass but not much else.

Again. And again.
Dusk to dusk. Ash to ash.

Someone says, *It won't be long now.*
Someone says, *That's not true. I need you. Your cats need you. Don't we count?*
Someone calls every morning. Worries every night.
Someone tells her husband, *It's breathtaking, really. Her isolation.*
A father. A sister. A neighbor. A friend.

Someone feels an unruly mix of rage and love and picks up a pencil. A camera. A phone. Trying to make sense of it. Of her.

(A definition of art?)

This life in another state. This voice on the other side of the phone. This essay.
Someone draws a sparrow. A groundhog. A king. A clown.
The lines are delicate.
Everyone has someone.
Someone who has no one.
Right?
Someone is startled awake now in the middle of the night.

but on Mars they dream of blue skies
by Jacqueline Simon

the sky was orange. a long-held grievance of daylight and flames.
silence. this silence. is barely secular. do you think the Plum trees will forgive us?
today's not the day to use armageddon. orange day. already built—still building
ruins.

you want a spectacle? this is your spectacle.
no Birds. no Bees. no florid Hydrangeas. my brain chemistry feels permanently
altered.

streetlights unaware of day. no explanation of the divine.
if you think of it, all gods are vengeful. should i have more questions?
young Turkey calling for flock-help. i've never heard a more alone sound.

Monster
by Cy Ozgood

I could sit all day
in this small room
getting smaller
watching the light
settle around me
like my body,
the room.

I am told it's my duty
to live
for those who could not.

It's good to be alive.
My body is good,
some rising serpent.

My god
pulled a fish
from my back
and the tenderness
got higher.

Whatever I would want
to fill this fruit with
is gone.

I live here
alone
and
everyone
is safe.

Cat's Tongue

by Kathleen Winter

Finally she saw him again, at a college reunion. Four gaudy chandeliers in the
ballroom shivered out splinters of light; the music was southern-fried rock,
decades old and sounding worse than ever. In his unbearable thirst she'd given
him the last, the first, the only water from the spring of her body--a theatrical
gesture only they two could remember. He wore a long-sleeved blue cotton
shirt, as he and his brother had worn so often years before. Even the greying hair
shone gold above his lupine eyes, which found her through his thin-rimmed,
expensive, glasses, through the chattering crowd in between them. She wanted to
say something to him, to bite it into the base of his neck deftly causing a bacterial
infection, to sling the words at him with her cat's tongue, every syllable covered
with a million tiny barbs. They'd snag in the membranes lining his nose, his ears,
and fester there. She'd ask him if he knew what his brother had done. He was
her last link to his brother, the transparent mucous thread of white when an egg
is separated, to the brother who was not there enduring the music, not standing
restlessly beneath the lights feeling heat crawl across his skin like a sickening
insect, a tick. She wanted them both to know she remembered, she had not for-
given it. Now she stood next to him beside a round table draped in white rayon,
laden with a garish centerpiece and trays of meat, flesh sliced so thin she could
see through it. And miniature, delicate vegetables were gathered in edible ribbons, in intricate bows and knots, like bouquets in a doll-house. The ballroom is
inside the doll-house: the roof's been removed and now she's looking down into
it. She doesn't know anyone in there--anyone. And how would he know what
his brother had done? How could he know his brother? The next morning she'd
tried to pretend it hadn't happened, her pretending becoming the strangest crime
of all. *No, you did Not*, she'd insisted to the brother, receiving him into her body
before she never saw him again. To scare them away from cigarettes, her high
school had shown the students a film--a human lung was cut into delicate slices,
terrifically thin, on a steel machine just like one in a deli. The camera examined a
sliver: the lung tissue was elaborate, lacey, crystalline in disease, like the pol-
ished plane of a geode. If she sliced the muscle of her heart, would its grain be as
simple, as smooth, as these shavings of lox and prosciutto? No, she didn't care
for a cocktail. No, not a glass of wine. She wanted silence, ice water. She'd take a
swallow, lick and lick and lick and lick the thin flesh of her forearm with her cat's
tongue, smoothing the cool damp arm across her flushed face, wiping hair from
her eyes, and she'd talk to no one.

(Re)Generation Triptych
by Alison Lubar

I. Picking Strawberries in May, 1940
> *for Auntie Masae*

While they were picking strawberries,
I was listening for screams.
Every fifteen minutes,
as often as I would try to wait to run
to the bathroom to wash the sticky witness
of poverty from my hands,
the manual labor of a ten year old,
> I would listen for the screams
of women in the field
who came across
a garter snake.
> Helpless, the snake,
and helpless, the women,
and helpless, us who waited
> for a December
> to change our lives,

but for now, I pinch the strong,
thin stem and place
each freckled reminder of my life
in a basket.
> I save the good ones for the top,
> and the bruised sweat underneath,
> blemished by no fault of their own.

I am not unhappy. I wait for the screams,
better at picking snakes than strawberries.

A Bookseller in Toronto
by Marcie Shleslinger Beyatte

My day starts with a woman rapping her knuckles on the front door in search of
a book for her brilliant three-year-old.

"Now I'm sure you hear this all the time, but my granddaughter really is as-
tounding. So gifted! What have you got for her?"

I hold books outside the open door like offerings but most are rejected as too
juvenile. As a result of the ravages of age, my back aches every time I reach down
to grab a book from the bottom shelf. The woman is eventually thrilled with
"Goodnight Stories for Rebel Girls," by Elena Favilli, a book I would normally
suggest for a young lady over eight.

There are countless brilliant three-year old's these days as well as accomplished six-year old's reading at a ninth-grade level. Imagine the pandemic incubating all this talent! My task is to find the appropriate book while the customer shivers in the snow. Sometimes I get it right on the first try, but I often have to present many titles while the cold wind makes my eyes water.

When customers call ahead, my job is easier. These are the folks who have a clearer idea of what they want from the warmth of their living rooms.

" I'm putting a package together for my friend who just left the hospital after a severe episode of depression. Can you make some recommendations? She likes dogs."

I take her number and call her back with some ideas; photo books and travelogues, lighter reading such as "Miss Benson's Beetle" by Rachel Joyce and because her friend is a dog lover, I suggest Mary Oliver's "Dog Songs" along with a dog-themed jigsaw puzzle. I include a throw blanket made of alpaca and some Canadian made herbal bath salts that smell of orange blossoms and spring. I complete the package with a handmade card. My customer thanks me and promises to come by later in the day to pick up her order.

Like most people these days, meaningful human contact is missing from my life. That is why I jeopardize my health every weekend to ride the subway to work, a calculated risk I have decided is worth taking.

Jane, a voice I only know over the phone, called a few weeks ago to special order Anne Patchett's book, "This is the Story of a Happy Marriage". I asked her if she had read Anne's essay, "My Three Fathers" printed in a recent New Yorker. She hadn't and was delighted to hear about it and told me about another non-fiction piece of Ms. Patchett's which I hadn't read called, "These Precious Days."

The following week, Jane tapped on the door to give me her copy of the magazine. I was reminded of my old bookselling life, full of surprises and moments of connection.

Geoff, a long standing customer pops by the door to check-in and we share stories and photos of our pandemic puppies, hoping they can meet one day. We both marvel at "Red Comet, the Short Life and Blazing Art of Sylvia Plath" by Heather Clark and confess to each other that at 1,152 pages, we will probably only read portions of it.

Some days I'm the grumpy bookseller who is impatient after holding up ten birthday cards to an indecisive customer who is searching for a funny card. And one day, when restrictions eased slightly and I could let a few customers inside, I I lost it when a customer refused to wear a mask.

The woman said," You work in a bookstore. Are you not educated? Don't you realize this virus is all manufactured and wearing a mask is useless? You should read a few of the books on your shelves."

I was shaking by the time she left, and I confess that I used a four-letter word directed towards a customer for the first time in my career.

But I'm a softie when kids come to the door with a bag full of change and want to buy a gift for their friend. Even though we stopped taking cash at the start of the pandemic, I make an exception. And the coins are rarely exact.

My wish is that someday soon I won't have to act like a cop, making sure that customers are sanitizing, staying far enough apart and haven't exceeded the posted number of bodies allowed in. I can simply welcome people back into the store.

Even, especially, the maskless woman.

And when that lady who refuses to wear a mask returns, I will try to summon up my kindness, remembering that some people are having a harder time than me. The pandemic takes its toll in ways that are invisible and not contagious but it teaches some of us patience.

Toward the Vicinity of Childhood
by J. J. Steinfeld

Caught in adult traffic
a harried, misshapen philosopher
contemplating failures
and falling short
of even modest loftiness
amidst horns berating thought,
fumes throttling breath,
you seek childhood safety
your parents' arms and voices
gentle traffic cops at work.

Nothing in the dark
can uncomb your hair
or sadden your eyes
if you whistle a brave tune
into the face of anything
bigger or louder than yourself
that's what your father taught
his gentle arms
a whole planet of protection
he whistling along with you.

Your mother
equally gentle
dealt with fear differently
sometimes the tunes were frozen

but the fears would not scatter
she patient and mystical
with her teachings.

Screech of brakes
close call
spit three times
the way your mother taught you
to defuse any fright
or abrupt horror
day or night
your own personal therapy
instant, just add water.

A lifetime of foreboding and jolts
and betrayals of the ordinary
you have learned to deal
with the horrors
and sudden frights:

spit and repeat
repeat and spit
your mouth is dry.

Then you whistle your brave tune
your hair nicely combed
your eyes glimmering joy
and you drive away
toward the vicinity of childhood.

Letter With Missing Parts
by L.A. Johnson

                    warning sirens
wail again at the power plant
and I can no longer see
the stars. I have waited too long
to write
           and for that, I am sorry

Ivy clings to the side
the house   covering
and I don't know how to
make it stop.

The light in the bathroom
has been out for weeks
too high for me   to touch
even when I jump. Do you
remember

                    string lights
when we walked late past dinner
under redwoods, talking
of danger   testing small bombs

in the language between us,
how easily our words split
a house   a lip
Hour gone warm, how beautiful
you were   the moonlight
sharpening inside your mouth

I am sorry
I used to think   of my body
as the only thing I could give,
a garden of orange flowers.
Let them wait.
They hunger in the shade.

The Owls
by Natalie Dunn

It's more like bird *listening*, my friend said when I told her I wanted to get into birdwatching. Birds being one of those things you don't notice until suddenly, you do.

It was dark and I was in bed when I heard a shrill squawk. I picked up my phone, *shrill squawk at night*? I watched a video of someone lowering an owl out of their apartment window with a Swiffer. Another where a barn owl appears silhouetted like a ghost flying between the clouds.

You heard them? My neighbor asked when, in the morning, I stared up at the red-woods around our apartment like I was looking for something. He pointed up to the date palm across the street and told me two barn owls had been living there for years. I squinted my eyes until I could see two white ovals asleep in a hollow part of the tree.

First it was the owls. Then in the spring, the hummingbird who worked paral-lel to me. I watched her collect pine resin and twigs the size of cherry stems for her minuscule nest. Sometimes she would come up to the window as if asking whether she could trust me with it. In the summer a fledgling crow wobbled on the sidewalk in front of our apartment for a week before taking flight. I named it Baby Crow and Willy dug up worms for it to eat even though I thought he shouldn't. FLEDGLING CROW, I wrote in blue sharpie on a piece of cardboard because people kept trying to save it, thinking it had a broken wing.

*

I'm at a reading, I mouth to Willy over my computer screen when he walks in the door and looks at me like he's not exactly sure where I am. I'm on the couch and I'm not. I'm inhabiting my square in a large swath of squares. My tangerine-orange sweater a kind of anchor for my eyes that wander in gallery view.

Sometimes I pin people's videos at random not when they're talking but just to watch them. When I tell my sister this she gives me a look as if I'm doing something illegal. It does feel strangely intimate, like watching someone through a crack in the door. But I like to fill them in. The shade of green on their wall tells me what kind of person they are, the snow outside tilts them north. I imagine their room, their house, the street they live on. Maybe it's to push against this feeling I have when I leave my square—that I've been everywhere all at once and nowhere at all.

*

The other night my friend Shayda and I met up halfway between our houses like we usually do to walk. We took each other to some of the places in the neighborhood we like to come back to, that remind us in some way of where we are: the front yard filled with hundreds of wind chimes all clanging a different pitch, the Madrone tree that peels in the fall like a sunburn, the house on Milvia that is entirely blue—blue walls, blue trim, blue bottles that line the windows and catch little squares of light, even a blue trash bin in the front where the rest of the neighborhood's is black.

I love *them*, she says when I show her the owls. I knew she would. It's after dusk and they're huddled together in a blur. We stand there and watch them for a while until our necks get tired from looking up.

How to Disappear
by Cynthia Randolph

In the dead bishop pines beside our house
owls are nesting. At 3 am they call
to one another, which sounds exactly
like someone impersonating two owls.
When the moon is full, I go outside and stare
into the darkness to look for them
and again see nothing. Last night
the wind was so strong
I feared the studio we are building
would lift off the ground
like a kite. We had just cut holes
in the walls for windows. It was open,
exposed. I had a dream of my mother's house
an excavator had ripped off the door
and cored out the insides. It was all beams
and drifting papers and arguing from within.
A man came out yelling, so I walked away

down River Road, towards nothing.
I have maybe ten photographs
of my mother, and also her yearbook
which I took secretly, and never returned.
It is off-white and tattered
with words I never noticed before
on the spine, The Gleam. It smells
how an old memory should smell. Everyone
looks the same. Navy blue dresses, Peter Pan
collared blouses. I worry I will not recognize her
or will see her and miss her afresh. When I find her
in a photograph, she is sitting with three women
working on the school newspaper.
Her hair pulled back.
Her placid smile.
She looks at me.
I wish I could see her hands.

For My Cousin Manny Who Died In Prison
by Cintia Santana

a cell   (my cousin's)
a heart

inside   inside
his heart
(inside
a cell)   he sold   my cousin
a cluster   (my cousin)   (a heart
of cells   inside)
           (he was   (inside
arrested   not   a cell)
           so old)   suffered

(like
a tack   inside   (ever
to the heart   (too)   since
the arrest   he sold   he was
inside   not
the heart)   inside   so old)
   ;   a block
(a tic   (a cluster
a tock   of cells)   inside
then not)   a sale   a cell
           (inside   a heart
           a cell)
                    at rest
           inside a block
           (block a)   (my cousin's)
           a cluster
       —way back
           blocked—
           an attack
           (inside
           a cell)
           an arrest
           (inside)

Past

The Yellow Phone
by Ada Limon

That was the summer in Mount Lassen
that was the middle fork of the Feather River
still icy in its mountainous sloping.

Under eagle shadow and boulder shade,
my friend Sarah with an H and I would climb
the wild river that wended among the trees.

Up all night singing, as young ones do, some
raunchy song I made up a whole second half to
and to which we'd laugh, crazed insomniacs

drunk on being ten years old and free
in the old growth red fir forest, how hilarious
 it all was, nature and bodies, and night.

That was the summer before my father
remarried and she was not unkind, but
in truth, we were sometimes unkind to her.

We listened to the Beatles cassette in her cream-
colored car and learned all the words to Rocky
Raccoon and what even was a Gideon's Bible.

I thought it could go on like that, our backset
singing the whole highway home to the hot valley
made burnt yellow by all that unstoppable sun.

Sarah and I were separated for only an hour
before the phone rang. Her handsome cousin
had died, a god who used to crush the high dive.

The yellow phone on the wall, the slew of pencils,
the things you look at when death enters before
you know what death even is. He was a child.

We were children. And here is the debt I carry:
I blamed her cousin for dying, blamed the motorcycle,
blamed the speed, raged against him, newly gone

and yet still shining wet on the diving board where
I had seen him last. I don't remember what I said,
an awful word, something forbidden, and my poor

sweet friend who knew me so well and who I
was bound to from birth, sobbed and it wasn't
just the crying that made me angrier, it was what

she said, *This is why I can't tell you hard things.*
To be clear, I don't even know if I apologized.
But I knew something true about myself then:

I meet grief with rage. I have carried that receiver
in my chest for over thirty years, her voice
at the other end, the phone cord ripped from the wall.

A Mouthful of Disappointment
by Maya Alexandria

I know I exist because I eat existential jambalaya
hoping it will taste of the sage advice given to me
by my papa on the bayou while singing to crickets
as soft as his willowing beard kissing my cheek;
but really, it tastes of hollow gumbo served on
a cold spoon, stewing my brain like the mixing
of car horns speaking over my brother telling me
how our father died alone in a hospital bed.

When the rice of your jambalaya reduces into roux
it's time to throw out the whole pot.

Inspired by Terrance Hayes' *American Sonnet for My Past and Future Assassin*
["Probably twilight makes blackness dangerous"]

How Can I Make Things Easier For You?
by Jo'kia Mc Call

When I was 10
I asked my mom to change my name to Vanessa.
It hurt my feelings when teachers kept dropping my name
like it was cement.
So I turned into clay
and little white hands tried to turn my hair into European art.
So I permed it to make it easier for them the next time I slept over.
Little white boys said I was too dark
so I hid from the sun.
When I got older
I changed my voice to get that job
perms weren't enough
I bought more hair
And when I saw real art
loud and vibrant
dark and unapologetic
I told my white friends I didn't know her.

Sun. Rise.

For Sina Ghanbari
by Siavash Saadlou

Held inside Evin, Iran's prison of favor,
you threatened the guards with your life,
your only ammunition—threatened
to annihilate your 22-year-old self
if freedom weren't going to be granted
before dawn, at which point you
were going to leave the house—
first thing in the morning—
to buy freshly baked naan and greet
your neighbors; at which point your mother
would have been preparing a pot of Persian tea,
expecting you…like every mother who believes
without seeing—believes that her child
will come back home in one piece.

This was your moment of mutiny
against the marooned marvels of life,
against the civilities of sanity and silence.
With every sunrise comes the killing
of another budding soul, the departure
of life as though it were never there.
And then, inanimate, insentient,
the city and its citizens go about their business.

Boston, March 2018

Prayer Beads
by Kiran Bains Sahota

It was you who once told me on the cement steps of your indigo house,
that all bodies of blood and bone hold a secret. Your white hair curled out of
your bun beneath the sheer ivory of your *chunni,* and your spectacles shone from
the glare of the sky. The beige cotton of your *kameez* and matching *salwar* had a
thousand little blossoms patterned along the fabric. Your chestnut vest was warm
where I clutched it in my palm and the tortoise-shell buttons gleamed as you
shifted your gaze back to me.

You threw an arm around me and pulled me into you, and I nuzzled
into the thick yarn of your vest.

Your hand came into view, your kara—a shining silver symbol of your
faith—dangling from your wrist. You opened and closed your palm quickly,
your wrinkly fingers fanning out like little pretend beams. You picked up my
hand to mimic the action, intertwining your fingers in mine and shaking them
with a funny excitement. We laughed after that. The squirrels scurried, the cats
drank from the milk you left them near the water heater, and the hummingbirds

sipped from the magenta wildflowers that bloomed from the soil by the bottom brick layer of the house.

I called you Mama. Because you, in the absence of my father, were my other parent. Why else call you Mama, if you weren't already the light that nourished those who sought you, like a mother to everyone?

But there came a day when I was barely fourteen, and you could no longer look at me and know that I was the great-granddaughter you raised as your own.

In the early morning, mom would leave for work as the stars were muted by the morning glow. I'd wake up to a low murmur outside the door and find you pacing around the house, an incense stick smoking from your hand. Like a wand, you waved it around images of Baba Nanak Ji, the Golden Temple, and the photos of the family along the living room wall. When I'd come out, you would wrap the spicy cloud around me, a prayer of protection flowing like sparks from your lips to the dissipating puff before me.

It reminded me of the peacock feathers that shimmered in a tall vase on the mantle. You collected them from the birds at the farm behind the house. They'd perch on the fence, squawk at the dog until she'd hidden under the porch, and shed their plumage upon the terrain. You told me how a third eye protects against nazar, or the evil eye, and showed me the strands of a feather up close. The slender stem was composed of brown and green strands; inside, a navy pupil was set against a bold cerulean iris that was so bright, it felt alive.

You kept them in the house to protect us, and never missed a sunrise to enchant us with your prayer. Sometimes now, I'll catch the scent of musk and clove and look for you in the hope that I'll find your body as bright as the birds with the feathers I now collect.

There was something my mom never told me when I lived in that indigo house. It was a truth she didn't want to believe, she tells me now, because it meant that you were human.

She didn't tell me then that your brain cells had stopped communicating the way they once knew how to. It started slowly. When you'd leave the gas running on the stove, the flames heating nothing but the air above them. When the bathtub flooded with water because you forgot you wanted to bathe. When you flew into a fit of rage neither of us had ever seen because you were convinced your son and his wife had schemes to take your house. She understood then, as I do now, that age had taken from you what we could not give back.

When I think of your hands now, I first picture clutching your palm as you lay on the thick mats in your youngest daughter's house in Turlock. The ventilator clicked and wheezed. Your eyes were closed. I was a month shy of sixteen, staring at your chest from the corner of the room as it rose slowly up, then down, and then repeated.

I finally came to sit by your side. After an hour, I finally stretched up. As my hand slid from yours, your fingers squeezed my skin. Your eyes were still closed and your chest rose with the same rhythm. I stared back at your hand, your butterscotch skin crinkly but still.

It was the last time I held your hand. It was the last time I felt whole.

My mom and I reside on the northern edge of town, in an ivory house with three rooms and a backyard with a budding palm tree. My room is dressed with lights and artificial flowers. Books of every hue line the shelves. Gel pens, piles of paper, and photos from my childhood litter my bed. The sight of them helps me believe that a story can start anywhere, from the time of one's birth, to tomorrow, where everything is unknown.

At twenty-five, in the midst of a pandemic that has stretched with time, I have become a child again. In the backyard, I run along the concrete and step into the sea of grass, a giant kid plotting the next chapter of my book by ranting and twirling as the sun glows hot and the birds flutter from out the foliage of the looming trees. The heat of the morning star is my joy—a reminder that new days are still arriving even as the globe is blanketed by pandemic stillness.

I whisk a wand of black pepper and amber through the hall. The stem of smoke lingers around the living room fireplace. On the mantle there's a black and white photo of you and Papa and a colored set of pictures of mom and me. There are burnt patches of paper on the hearth, their shriveled bodies once flat with scribbles. But I deemed them unworthy of remembering.

There's even a room in this house with some of your things, Mama. There's the portrait of the lion—his honey-brown mane painted in thin strokes of acrylic—that once hung over the couch in the living room. There's your wooden side table by the bed; the oak drawer with its brass handle holds a velvet pouch with your beads in it.

I imagine you're in there praying, with your eyes closed and your lips moving to the Granthi's words as if you have the scripture in front of you. I slide my back against the wall and stare at the closed door, imaging myself opening it. It groans lightly at the first crack, and I peek inside to see your white *chunni* draped over your bun and around your shoulders. Your prayer beads—little wooden orbs collected along a string—lightly sway as your palms press together, your wrinkly lids closed.

Landscape with Waterfall and Ibises
by Ellen Kombiyil

Each day
ladies clawed

up moss-hung rocks
to hightail it to

blacktop through miles of
empty forest. It was

always summer, daddy
like a waterfall

crashed into
pools of bikinis.

It was the time
of year when hatchlings

fell from
nests—did she

mean to
escape? that girl

vaulting
into the flume?

Ma watched me watch
a medic stretcher

her off not bloody
but broken, her glass

eyes open
like dolly

who never
sleeps but all night

stares at the curtains —
like that, I

eyeballed the rocks. Forget it
ma said, it's

too dangerous, so we'd
swim and

swim in mist
piped in among trills

of mechanical
ibises. Onlookers tossed

pennies heavy
and cold that I

dove for, my fingers
gouging blue

paint chipped from the pool
floor. I wedged pennies

into toe gaps stuffed
the lining of my

bikini top till
it burst and they jabbed

at my breasts I crammed
them into my mouth

I'd have guzzled more
if I could. *Help*, I meant

102

to shout to the girl,
mum, wading

near the pool's
edge, her wishes

moneyless. I
shoved her

my dripping
fistfuls—*I have*

nowhere
to put this.

Solve for Ex
by Alison Lubar

What is an X   except
a crossroads?   An axis
        precedes the signature line:
                                coordinates
        kissing once then limitless
distance.   Two lines make
        four directions,   spend
timespace   in   creation:

a mark. The point where it begins,
        and you walk into the sunlight
[I really did love you]
        and turn back once
[I will wait here]
        and forget the deadbolt
[please never come back]
        I pray the car doesn't start
[my life is here]
        and still be relieved at its grey rumble:
[we have run our course]
        You forget to call.

Let's hope our intersection
        was more universe than earth:
we   extend   infinitely
        instead of circling
back to   this origin,
never back   to marking   the spot.

Pressed

by Simone Muench and Jackie K White

On a sheetless mattress, immobile and
undone, I was marked for ruin. I drowned
in dread, became a stain, a container
of shatter, of "I don't matter." I'm told to
muzzle that memory with pillow plush,
and smother all the old mouths' carping
as I'm pressed into performance, pushed to play
that old game perfectly. Now, I turn the mouth

into spewing glass. The anatomy of a rupture.
I burn. I bellow. I say no I say no I say no.
This is the season of the scalpel, not nostalgia
This is the year of scraping out hauntings.
I said no. Now I shove that ghost into the fold,
press back, iron the sheets of my choosing.

The Psychic's Prediction

by Shelley Walden

A psychic once told me that things in my life would happen in threes.
Which is how I found myself flying to Mexico for the third time in three years,
hours after my third miscarriage. I should have canceled the trip, but I was a
bridesmaid in a friend's wedding and couldn't abandon her.

So I hid my grief and zipped myself into an emerald bridesmaid dress,
the one I'd ordered a size too big to hide a growing belly. As I walked down the
aisle, I bled. But my trauma was invisible to the crowd, buried beneath styled
hair, fake eyelashes, and red lipstick.

As I watched my friend say her vows, I realized I was tired of waiting
for my babies to die. If I was strong enough to walk down that aisle when all I
wanted to do was collapse in bed, then maybe I was strong enough to conquer
the miscarriage demon. And even if I couldn't, I owed it to myself to try.

I began my fight with the hardest step, confronting my grief. I broke
the first rule of Miscarriage Club: do not talk about your miscarriages. Over the
next few weeks, I told family, friends, and strangers. I also found a therapist who
helped me process my emotions. I hated feeling my pain, but I did it anyway.

I switched acting classes and dove into Meisner, a technique I'd avoided
for years. The method was designed to get students out of their head and into
the present moment. We were encouraged to confront our emotions by using "I"
statements. I repeated phrases like "I am anxious. I am angry. I am sad," over
and over again till they lost their power. I also labeled the emotions of others:
"You are furious. You are hurting. You are strong." Watching the other actors, I
realized I wasn't the only one suffering: we were all a little broken.

Then I tackled my health. One miscarriage was a fluke, two was bad
luck, but three — that was a problem. I couldn't keep doing the same thing and
expect different results. So I started seeing an acupuncturist who stabbed me

twice a month. Based on her advice, I abandoned vegetarianism and added beef, super greens, and Chinese herbs to my diet.

I also experimented with mumbo jumbo. Because I was living in Los Angeles and surrounded by hippies and hipsters, I began wearing stones to help with fertility, including red carnelian, moss agate, and moonstone. I tried sound bath yoga. The vibration of the bowls relaxed me, but my uterus didn't feel any cleaner. So I went to a spa in Koreatown and tried a V-steam, a Gwyneth Paltrow–endorsed treatment that involved crouching over a steaming pot of herbs. I figured it couldn't hurt, but I was wrong. I spent half the session trying to convey to an employee who didn't speak much English that my lady bits were on fire. The other half was spent hovering over the pot, like a chicken nesting atop an egg.

Then I entered the research phase. I scoured message boards, looking for advice, and read Mark Zuckerberg's Facebook posts, searching for clues as to how his wife had a baby after three miscarriages. After finding nothing of use on the Internet, I moved on to books. I read a fertility book that said castor oil packs could regulate hormones, so I put them on my belly every few days, even though they stained my couch. I read *The Life-Changing Magic of Tidying Up* and discarded eight bags of stuff to make room in my life. Then I read *Eat, Pray, Love*, and decided to follow the author's lead and petition the universe for what I wanted. I wrote a letter asking for a healthy child and included fake signatures from all the people I thought would support my cause: friends, family, and the Dalai Lama, because he seemed like an awfully nice guy.

Then I prayed: to Jesus, Mary, and all the Saints I could remember. I didn't pray to God, though. I was too mad at him.

Next, I sought out the miracle of modern-day medicine. My blood was drawn again and again until I had more needle pricks than a voodoo doll. My uterus was injected, scraped, and examined. The infertility doctor found not one problem, but three: low Vitamin D levels, a mutation that made it difficult to digest folic acid, and uterine inflammation called endometritis. The doctor said my eggs were geriatric, too, but since I was only thirty-three I refused to believe that. I was prescribed three different antibiotics for the endometritis, which I took over three weeks.

When the antibiotics cleared my system, my husband and I tried again. But this time, we had modern medicine on our side, including Clomid, progesterone, and baby aspirin. After Clomid, the doctor did an ultrasound and discovered I had three viable eggs. I had the potential to lose three children this time.

We conceived after the first dose of Clomid. Getting pregnant was never the problem, though. As the ultrasound approached, I sensed that I was carrying more than one baby. What I didn't know was if their hearts were beating.

At the appointment, the doctor assured me she saw two heartbeats. I asked her to double check. "There are two," she said. "I'm sure."
I'd never had a fetus with a beating heart before, let alone two. I tried not to get too excited, for there was no telling how it would end. Though my heart yearned for two "rainbow" babies — children born after a miscarriage — my head knew better.

The first trimester crawled on and I began to feel nauseated. I even threw up a few times, something that never happened with my previous pregnancies. I'd never been so excited to hurl. But a few days later I spotted some blood and panicked.

When I went in for my next ultrasound, there were still two heartbeats.

The doctor said the same thing at the next ultrasound and the one after that. For the first time ever, I entered my second trimester and then, finally, my third. My anxiety level decreased as my belly grew, but it never disappeared.

When I reached thirty weeks, my husband and I moved from Los Angeles to New Mexico. Since I was too pregnant to fly, we drove. I was terrified of going into labor in the middle of a desert. It didn't help that I was the size of a sumo wrestler and that strangers frequently said, "Any day now."

The first day we weathered 115-degree heat and arrived at our destination safely. But the next day, I leaked water. When we arrived in Albuquerque, I called a nurse and was told to go directly to the hospital.

I was examined and told my membranes had prematurely ruptured and that the chances were high I would deliver within the next seventy-two hours. The absolute longest I would be allowed to go was thirty-four weeks, at which time the infection risk would be too high to keep the babies inside me. No matter what, the babies were guaranteed a stay in the neonatal intensive care unit. I burst into tears; I had done everything in my power to have healthy babies and it still wasn't enough.

The nurses pumped magnesium through my veins to stop the labor and gave me a steroid to strengthen the babies' lungs. That afternoon, as I battled contractions, I looked out the hospital window and saw a double rainbow peeking through dark clouds. It felt like a sign, except I'd stopped believing in them.

I made it through the night. The next day, I was moved to a long-term unit. The room, with its drab walls, slow Internet, and rubbery food, became my whole world. I hung a calendar on the wall and crossed out the days. I made it past the first seventy-two hours and the seventy-two hours after that. My husband spent every night in the hospital by my side, sleeping on the most uncomfortable cot known to man.

Twice a day, I was hooked up to a machine that monitored the babies' heartbeats. It was a form of torture, waiting there motionless as the nurse struggled to locate that galloping sound. They told me it was hard to find their hearts because they moved too much, but I worried something was wrong.

Every morning a doctor checked on me, and he was always surprised I was still there. One day he said, "I wish all mothers fought as hard for their children as you do." But it didn't feel like a choice; it felt like survival. After so much death, my will to fight for life was strong.

As the days passed, I couldn't help but cling to something the psychic told me years before, on a dark New Orleans street corner. After saying things would happen to me in threes, she added, "And you will have twins." Was she right? Or did she, like many oracles, leave out a crucial detail?

At thirty-three weeks, my body surrendered to an infection and the doctor decided to deliver via emergency C-section.

"Will I be able to see them when they're born?" I asked a nurse.

"No," she said. "They'll be taken to intensive care and you won't see them right away — unless they are healthy enough to cry."

I was given a spinal and cut open. As they tore my daughter out of my uterus, I heard her piercing cry. A minute later, I heard my son's. They were the most beautiful sounds I'd ever heard. I'd given birth to two children with beating hearts.

And the curse of three was broken.

1940, Rodmell, Sussex, England
by Natascha Graham

The pages of a book shudder, flutter, then turn, all at once
a pen rolls to the floor
it is not the dream, nor the wind
that wakes her
but the low call in the air, in the sky
of her name, *perhaps*, or a sound, that falls over itself as it comes, *like* her name,
whispered too quickly between the creak of the floorboards
and the opening of the door
she seeks it
outside the night is high and black
clear and drawn all over with everyone else's stars
she, a silhouette framed in an open door, half in, half out listening to the far, far
away rumble of German bombers, of London burning, of the sky falling
but still, she hears it, a murmur, a snake in the grass, a feather falling, a moment
passing from one page, to the next

The Chrysanthemum
by Daisy He

My mother came back as a flower. A chrysanthemum. On a clear day
after the winter began, the flower blossomed on the balcony of my apartment in
Shanghai, and I knew that it was my mother coming back. Its white, slim, curved
petals stretched; it breathed and trembled; its gesture didn't change; it wanted
to say something but it just stopped, and in the end it only sighed. I heard the
flower sigh, just like I had heard my mother sigh in the last moment of her life.

My mother died a couple of years ago of leukemia. Before her passing
my mother had lived with me for years. Like many Chinese families, we had
three generations living under one roof – my mother, my husband and I, and our
child. My mother used to plant flowers like daffodils or roses on the balcony, and
the chrysanthemum was her favorite. My mother liked sewing, and she made
cute shirts for my little son and cotton pajamas for me. She used to be the one
who took care of most of our housework. The kitchen was her territory, and she
often didn't like my husband and I to lay a hand in it while she or Aunt Cheng
cooked. Aunt Cheng came every afternoon to help us with cleaning and cooking.
She was not my aunt - in China every housework service worker is called aunt.
When things didn't turned out as she expected, my mother would keep nagging.
Sometimes she said to Aunt Wang, "Why haven't you got the dinner done yet?
Dinnertime is coming soon."

Shortly after my mother died, Aunt Cheng came to me and said: "I am
going to quit, because you mother is back at home now. When I am cleaning
or cooking, I feel that she stands behind me, nagging me, just like what she did
when she was alive. "

I felt my hair stood up on the back of my neck. Was my mother really
home? If so, how could I not know? Aunt Cheng was scared of the spirit, so she
left soon. I kept thinking of her words. My mother died in hospital, which was

seven miles away, to the west of the Huangpu River. She didn't die at home. How could she come back? Did she come back through under river tunnel or did she come back by ferry? It must be by ferry, I guessed, because the tunnel was busy and dark, not a good choice. But if she took the ferry, she had to leave the hospital, pass the crossroads downtown where cars honked, and walk a long way along the lanes with sycamore trees before she arrived at the ferry station. When the ferry took her to the middle of river, she would have a 360 degree view of the city. West of the river was the view of the old Shanghai bund built a hundred years ago, east was the landscape of magic towering skyscrapers. The gentle breeze on the river would have blown on her face as waves kept rising and tumbling and engines on boats rumbled. Soon she would have arrived at the destination. The ferry would have banged when it hit the dock. Upon hearing that loud sound, I would tell my mother, you have crossed the river, go ashore, walk along the Main Blvd, and turn left on the next green light. Keep going, soon you will find your home, our home.

I didn't believe Aunt Cheng's words until six months later when the chrysanthemum blossomed. I watched the flower. Her petals were slim and fragile. It seemed that she had used up all her strength to blossom. She had to travel all the way from her roots in the dark earth to the air in the daylight. The flower said she was happy. "Give me some water," the flower begged me. I pitied her juiceless petals and watered her instantly. I watered her day after day. She bloomed more widely, and stretched her petals more exuberantly. She blossomed for a month.

*

Perhaps there is a cure for my mother's disease now, but there was not then. Her last chemotherapy started after the New Year of 2014. I drove her from home to the hospital – across the river tunnel, passing an elevated road, and taking an exit to one of the busiest areas in the city. One had to drive very slowly and cautiously when entering the bustling streets and winding lanes, where bicycles and pedestrians passed by very close to the car.

The ward was a large room with around eight beds. A woman sat on the bed near door, brushing her gray hair as we entered the room. Around each bed there was a curtain, which was to keep the privacy, but most of time the curtains were left open. My mother's bed was in a corner of the ward, near the window, where we could see the bare branches of sycamore trees against hazy winter sky. A dust web was dangling under a vent on the ceiling above her bed. A janitor came and swept away the hanging dust with a wet towel tied on the end of a broom. My mother took out her mug, toothbrush and her reading glasses from a suitcase, and put them on a bed stand. It felt like we had stopped at an inn.

"I will be with you shortly," Dr. Xu appeared at the gate of ward. He was a dark-skinned, stern-faced man, around 60 years old. Dr. Xu and a nurse pulled the curtains around the patient's bed, where they were going to do a lumbar puncture. Everyone in the ward became silent. I had watched a nurse did this with my mother before. A lumbar puncture was a procedure to draw a patient's spinal fluid for diagnosing a disease or defining its progression. A needle tube pierced between two lumbar bones in a patient's lower back. That's what Dr. Xu and the nurse were doing. A couple of minutes later, I heard Dr. Xu say: "Wonderful! You are such an awesome patient." "You are such an awesome doctor," the patient replied. The two praised each other.

Dr. Xu came to us. He greeted my mother with a smile, and it was soothing to see a smile from a stern face. "The white cells will definitely drop after the therapy. We are doing this here every day. In a couple of weeks you will be home as a healthy person," he assured my mother.

Each time when Dr. Xu came to talk to us, he was nice and patient, and his tone always made us see a hope. It reminded of me what was said in an aphorism about a good doctor - "to cure sometimes, to relieve often, to comfort always."

My brother and I never tell my mother that she had leukemia, thinking the name of the terminal illness would destroy her. My mother only knew that it was a blood disease, and that every once a while, she needed to came to the hospital for a regular treatment. In retrospect, I asked myself, if I could go back one more time, would I tell her the truth? Did she have the right to know her own illness? Whether the true reason was we didn't want her to worry or we just didn't want to be troubled by her worries? People would sometimes show amazing courage when coping with issues of life and death. Could we underestimate her? But even if I were given the second chance, I felt I simply couldn't speak the word Leukemia to her, as that was too hurtful. I would clench my teeth, and swallow the word down. "Do you really think your mother never know her illness?" my uncle, her younger brother, once said. "She knew every minute," he added. My mother knew everything - how it affected her body, how dizzy she felt, how easily she bled or bruised, or how frequently she felt exhausted. She knew everything about the disease except its label, and I didn't know much about it except its label.

A year before my mother was diagnosed, she once read her medical check report, which showed pretty much nothing abnormal except a slight anemia. We thought that was caused by a nutrition problem. My mother put aside the report and suddenly said, "Protect me." She might have sensed a coming danger, but at that moment I had no clue why she said that, and nor did I know what to do to protect her.

My mother once worked as a horticulturalist, planting and studying citrus and grapes before she retired. When I was a child, we lived in a large orchard where there were citrus trees everywhere. One of my mother's job was to circle an area around a tree and count the number of citrus flowers and fruits that dropped. She did experiment with the trees using different fertilizing and pest controls methods. Her purpose was to protect the flowers from dropping, so that they could grow into edible fruits. She spent much time in the fields, and her shoes always had mud when she came back home from work.

My mother believed in dialectical materialism, a part of Marx Philosophy, which was preached everywhere in China. Most people in my mother's generation believed that the world's essence was material, and that "religion is the opium of the people." She didn't believed there was a soul. She said that after people died, the body just decayed and decomposed, and became fertilizer in the earth.

I avoided talking with her about any religious views. She saw my Bible at home and knew I read it. She was a little bit horrified, for she might think that the book must be related to "opium." That feeling made me very uncomfortable so I didn't say anything to her regarding my belief. But she was still my mother. I loved her, and she loved me. When she was ill, I earnestly prayed that

God would heal her. I was devastated to see her health kept declining. But I still continued to pray, thinking that I would be more hopeless if I believed nothing.

In spite of adding antibiotics, despite that we were cautious on her food, my mother still had an intestinal infection when her chemo was close to an end. She had very high fever and severe diarrhea for a couple of days.

In those day, I sat by the side of her bed. Her check flushed because of the fever. A cooling patch was on placed her forehead. Her hair was wet from sweating and I kept drying it with a towel. From time to time I placed a mercury-in-glass thermometer under her tongue to monitor her temperature. Her body sometimes shivered. "I am cold," she said, "give me one more blanket." Then I put a blanket, my coat, everything we could find in the ward to keep her warm.

Nurses showed me my mother's temperature data and charts, which was stressful. Dr. Xu warned if the fever lasted for more than two weeks, the patient would have fewer chance to survive. On the Chinese Lunar New Year's Eve, I didn't go back home. One patient's sister gave me a folded recliner chair, and I slept by my mother's bed.

There was only one bathroom on the ward. It was near the door. The next afternoon when I went out of the bathroom, I heard someone behind me say, "Could please close the door? I am eating." It was from the gray-haired woman whose bed was near the door. She sat on the bed, with a plate full of food placed in front her. I turned back to the door and found it wasn't closed – how could I forget? "I am so sorry." I closed it. She continued with her dinner. She ate her food slowly and gracefully. I got a glimpse of a few piece of smoked fish on her plate.

The next morning when I came to the ward, I found the gray-haired woman's bed was empty. My mother fever had come down. "Come close," my mother waved to me and said. "I've got something to tell you." "What happened?" I asked.

"Look at that bed near the door, the patient passed away last night. Septicemia," she said.

I was stunned. She was the one who told me the day before to close the door of the bathroom, who enjoyed the smoke fish in her plate. Suddenly she was gone.

"I had such a high fever last night," my mother continued, "that I felt I kept rising. I had risen so high as if I were in a dream. Then there was someone's hand pushing down. The hand was on my head, so I was coming down. I kept coming down till I was back to my bed. You see, my fever has come down. I know it must be the hand of your God. I believe there is a God now."

I stood there in awe. I knew my mother would never lie to me, but something prevented me from inquiring further about what she had told me. I couldn't imagine how she could rise so high, and what a hand it was to push her down. Perhaps that miracle only belonged to those who had been once close to death. I felt feared but blissful. I turned my eyes away from my mother, watching the empty bed where the woman eating smoked fish had slept. All the bedding was changed. The sheets were neatly laid, without a winkle.

After my mother left the hospital, we enjoyed a brief period of peace. She could go out for a walk. We even took my son to a cartoon film history exhibit. We watched together an episode of the *Monkey King*, and a short film named the *Little Tadpole Looking For Mother*, which was the one I had watched as a child. My mother was in a good mood all the time. When we left, she started to sing a song that she learned years ago. She hummed the melody all the way when we drove home. Her face glowed. It was one of our happiest days. Both of us forgot the hospital, forgot the medicine, forgot leukemia, and forgot Dr. Xu.

My mother died a few months later after the spring. She fell into a coma one night. In the last few hours, we watched the monitor showing that her heartbeat rose up to 160 times per minute. My brother and I were with her. My mother's heartbeat made me think of an athlete who was dashing to her final destination. We talked to her. In the last moment, before her breath was gone, I heard her sigh. The sigh was so clear as if she were saying, "It happens so fast. I have to say good-bye to you now." I held her head in my arms. On the monitor her heartbeat dropped rapidly to zero. A nurse came and pulled out an electro-cardiogram with a long flat line, a report they collected to add to a dead patient's file. I watched my mother's face, and felt the death was so solemn and quiet.

*

That winter, my mother came back as a flower. The chrysanthemum. Her astringent scent and dazzling whiteness distracted me from my sorrows. I watched her, and watered her. I still had the ache of the loss, but every minute she blossomed, I felt strangely comforted. The comfort came from a mother's love, from her incarnation as a beautiful chrysanthemum. The flower blossomed for a month before her petals turned into a pale pinkish color, before she finally withered. I didn't see her anymore.

Ode to My Undoing

after Muriel Rukeyser
by Jacqueline Simon

The baby was born with vestigial wings. I
was frightened of course. Unknowing who would
betray this avatar of transgression. Or have
I realized who betrayed whom? Who liked
the feel of stones in their mouth to
tether their myths? Why couldn't I try,
with bruised certainty, to save it? There were those
amongst us who only saw molting wings
and dry rivers. I was never by myself,
never able to wash the child. It
would have folded wings over my thumb. Would
have yawned, revealing bird's tongue. Would it have
seen my gaze and turned its head aside, been
starkly naked with trembling wings better
than eyelids? But I was no better than
those wings to fly. I was no better than this.

Community

The Possibility of the Edges
by Ada Limon

Because the shadow holds the heaviness of branch,
the weight of last year's leaves and before that, and before that.

Because the shadow stretches over the bedsheet like a sideways
figure holding tight to the twisting world.

Because the shadow feels so different depending on the slippery hour,
the taste of copper at the back of the mouth.

Because the shadow is where we used to make out, remember, a boot
shoved up against a barred window, secrets.

Because the shadow is where the fox lives, near the creek
where the water's just beginning to catch on.

Because the shadow is where you are you and I am me,
pillar of lights all gone, the lost unwieldy ache of armor.

If they ask, it was because the shadow was always
with me and it never felt like hiding, not lonely at all.

El Melancólico
by Jose Hernandez Diaz

A man in a Chicano Batman shirt rode his lowrider bicycle in the sunshine. It
was still technically winter, but in the afternoon, there was plenty of sunshine:
it was southern California. The man in a Chicano Batman arrived at the library.
He checked out Baudelaire's *Paris Spleen*. Baudelaire was his favorite writer, even
though he thought the Frenchman was kind of crazy. "Life is kind of crazy," the
man in the Chicano Batman shirt said. After he checked out the book, he went
home and read it. There was graffiti written on the walls and sewers of his barrio;
not a lot, but enough to scare the white people away. When the man arrived in
his apartment, he made a strong coffee and began flipping through the book. His
favorite prose poem was, "The Clown." Then, "The Stranger." "That Baudelaire
was one melancholy fuck," the man in a Chicano Batman shirt said; "just like
me."

When This is Over
by JoAnn Scandiffio

I'll untie
my shoelaces
leave my sneakers
among pairs of
new and worn
boots heels sandals
Enter the Zendo
Where I'll sit
next to a stranger
who carries
the scent
of bread baked
in an open oven
We'll chant
with one breath
for shoes lined up
in the hallway
for shoes
that did not appear
And those
who sit
on the sidewalk
barefoot
with their one bowl
who cannot say
when this is over

NEVER THE END

Genes Of 55 Million-Year-Old Sea Monsters Live Inside Us
by Sage Scrittore

and what of th breach — of sand fleas burrowed in th beach — wrecked whale
joined by shark carcass on th flat turquoise shore —make it about yr equinox

o spring; — purple bloom tranquilize me a bud of moonlight — yr meta
-morphosis, morphology of th loom — tributarily; — distance mouths a monster

th monster that wrecks and wreaks harm — i don't mention my generational line
not even as a story at parties — flotsam on th wall splattered like blood splatters

       a vase; —

faceless abalones, ear-shaped, lined with respiration — [   ]-of-pearls strung
like sibilance around a sibylline soothsayer's neck — in th sequel to this poem

there will be dragons — inapprehensible dragonflies — reprehensible cures
sometimes antidotes taste worse than poison

       have you had th monoclonal antibody treatment? i hear it does wonders
       for yr skin. our bodies made defensible by epidermal injection

epidemiology of blue light in our eyes — too much good news in th syringe tho
keep coming back for a mouthful of adversity — you know th way to a man's
pockets?

       his pockets; —

a shape composed entirely of ampersands — an ocean composed entirely of the
letter C
o chimera, god of monsters and monster of spring bloom; — when yr nest was
ransacked

did th hero let th children live, or did he cut them down too, seeing nothing but
claws and teeth?

An Attempt At Illuminating A Place In Los Angeles
by Bixby Jane

a vaguely white bird jumps from the top of a lone pine I do not have my glasses /
no ambulance for the fake crying boy his father keeps walking not looking back /
threads of string wither in rusted barbed wire looking northeast for now / every
unbuilt space in the queer bounded territories of vaguely public land where
resident grasses grow must be cut by May as required last year no one saw them
from across the river little moon men working their way up a pass giving the
mountain her state mandated crew cut / a Matilija poppy splayed open like a
fried egg on a hot sidewalk is already tired before summer comes to obliterate
us and the disease some people say / narrow window of light marks the shape of
petals on declivitous yellow shale / many shutters drawn seemingly forever hide
from us what we do not understand / the well-kept chaos of the garden where
they paint evil eyes in the knots of the trees feels like home / a Chinese Elm with

a hole in its trunk gives life an edge the ones inauspicious beginnings are prone
to / a Belgian Shepherd lying hog tied by the sun can pay no mind to the sweet
unfamiliar baby sounds on the other side of a thin wall / a Blue jay rests briefly
on a Colorless fire hydrant not colorless but with so many it's hard to be known
by one and multicolored sounds psychedelic in a sophomoric college sage kind
of way so it's colorless because we only give names to things of a dominant color
at least as a name for something using color / the corner of a roofline and a wall
wear a tinted west facing window just over a hedge that has taken the hill and
most of the dark house from here / watching curled fingers around chain link
fencing feels like something could shake us free from writing in this contorted
position a lawless yoga / the peeling paint of yard placard rhymes and the low
hum of commercial dogma where cable lines puncture siding fantastically coiled
on the outside of a likely decrepit interior a dirty rag hanging near the mailbox
blows but there is TV / is editorializing really just a euphemism for judging our
neighbors? / wishing someone could read aloud the 31 odd neon green post-it
notes stuck to the studio window above the garage / the people that take care of
their home may soon buy a can and paint their front door pink and orange like
the bougainvillea at the empty corner lot that everybody loves / a broken slab
foundation like a coffin on display is being taken by the hill and no one is struck
by this enough to break it up or paint a mural of flowers / now seeing a house
from below it makes sense / each day can be an eternity but an elegantly placed
root ball is a seat in the shade it is also next to dumpsters and Sonic ketchup
packets in the gutter and is also what no one asked for an anarchist public works
project / when shopping carts find their way to a final resting place under an
orange tree on a quiet street that is beautiful for now / all these walls we all know
people are behind but still it is quiet like the mostly people-less airplane overhead which we can be sure is essential

no one thinks the dogs that wander these streets go home after they take themselves for walks someone believes they do this one / picking up scents it seems
is a delicate art circling and moving on and knowing when to deft creatures if
left alone / rarely is food at the end of one of these threads it seems to be about
process more than anything maybe practice the kind we can only do alone / why
are these NOTICE OF INTENT papers always yellowed and fraying at the edges?
/ no one wonders what half-smile thinks when someone is writing in a booklet if
it were notes for a notice of intent which could be more or less the truth at least
enough to warrant just half of a smile that could explain what no one wondered /
writing against trash can lids is a bit weird someone hopes she's moved on even
if no one will / how did someone get an old trolley car in their backyard? it must
have been there before them or the house what a person the kind who would
leave it as an artifact / someone may not know any names or that anyone knows
theirs although no one has admired someones garden for a couple years and not
thought it auspicious to hear them talk finally with their neighbors about natives
and perennials / no one sleuths near an abandoned contemporary looking for
someone with bright white eyes and golden skin no one can see their high bone
structure keeps face as they read something on a laptop surrounded by their
yard work / they wear thick framed specs like a late career Eliot Gould although
they once looked like a Long Goodbye before they talked with their neighbors
and tended to the grounds and knit mandalas for the electrical poles and painted
eyes on trees.

Mt. Washington - April 10, 2020

Bros 4 Life
by Jasmine Kahlia

Timber Road - Julius' house.

Julius had always been the street-smart 1 out of the three of us. Me, Lima + Julius we were such a power trio before Lima lost life.

i was their lil bro. To them, It didnt matter i wasnt like other guys.

Julius's house was in front of the cemetery, no one came up to the house except me + Lima.

Poor house, broken house, lost on the way home, kinda house. Most people walked to the middle of Timber Road and turned into Crawley Road.

Most didnt even see the houses at the end, where Julius lived. Most didnt see Julius, didnt even look him in his slanted dark eyes, just shuddered past him, glad he didnt choose them as one of his victims, as they assumed black boys would simply do.

Julius was far away now; hidden. All he wanted on his birthday was 2 see my face again, before he left 4 good.

Our life was simple as it could be, complex as it could be - for us poor boys of colour in this unforgivin land. I needed 2 see Julius - a feeling unlike anything ive ever known stretched its way through my abdomen and stole my sense of security.

Me and Lima walked up every time, kickin our neon orange football between us as we trekked up the quiet road. Lima's soft black curls lifted back over his brown eyes, back lightly sweatin, but he always used 2 look slick even after a whole day on the pitch.

My stupid light brown hair sticked up, didnt wanna behave, so i often bleached the top and shaved the sides. i looked like a fuzzy coconut kid. My biceps were comin up bit by bit - but all the gym in the world couldn't make me take up space in the world like Julius and Lima naturally did.

My girl never complained but even still. U'd neva catch man ridin topless on my bike during the hottest days of summer like my bros often did.

Boys like me cant survive here - even if boys like me stayed quiet about everythin. Boys like Julius could without a 2nd thought.

Even my girl doesnt know everythin I been through 2 get here. But now, she's the only person I got left.

Lima leaving this world ripped a whole in me. Nothin, not even our memories, not even our music could bring peace in my head. Julius and I were the only ones that knew what truly happened. And that secret's gonna go 2 my grave.

To get across to see Julius, for the last time in my life, i had to go back to Silas Road.

My girl said she'll come with me. She's not street smart, neither am I, but she knows her way round much better than me. I cant focus on all these roads right now, knowin they cant mother me like i need to be mothered.

Seacrest Road - My Home

I'm the only one in our trio to know the pavestones up close on my ass, surrounded by a bin bag of my possessions, kicked out once again, never looked on with compassion, its easy to be upset all the time but i gotta b real. no one's ever wanted me. i tried 2 lay low and not get sucked into the system stuff again, cause kids like me - too young 2 live alone, too old to be homed again - find themselves truly lost.

I fingered this vintage ice pick my grandad left me before he died. it was beautiful, hand carved wooden handle from Belgium. I'm sure it was worth a bit, as it used to be kept displayed in a cabinet before grandad took it out to give 2 me. i always walk with it in my inner pocket and keep in this pencil case I stole from my last foster home.

washin my face and my underwear in Burger King bathroom, I came across Julius.

'Yo what u doin in the mens room?' his voice boomed over my head.

'surviving, bro' I said back.

'oh snap, I thought u was a girl.'

'most people do' i said back to Julius.

He didnt need to know yet anyway.

He bought me some fries and a drink and invited me to his- it was just him and his sister livin at home. I didnt ask questions.

Sitting in his room, playing Cypress Hill's album, a lean, kinda tall light skinned guy walked in. He kinda reminded me of what I think my dad looked. But my memory cant really conjure my dad's face anymore. it was years since i last saw him.

'Yo, kid. I'm Lima.' Stretching out his hand, I shook it lightly. 'What u called?'

I looked up at him - judging whether I should trust him just yet.

'Let's play football. 1-a-side.' I laughed at his dumb suggestion and we headed out to the park.

Julius didnt mind me crashin at his. Not like anyone was coming back for him and his sister. Little odd jobs keep them paying the bills so they dont get kicked out - and me helping out has eased things up, so it's calm.

Since then I've simply sofa surfed - im small enough and quiet enough that everyone just lets me crash.

Truedale Road - Warehouse.

Memories of bonfire night screams into me - i remember everything so vividly that i often just pull my girl closer and take a swig from my mini bottle of wray and nephews to try relax.

We were in our Tottenham Football shirts - Lima was wearing his yellow one, I was wearing my white one. We were gonna link up with Julian at our usual spot - the carpark on Holybush Road to skate around and play our the new Drake mixtape.

Akram from K7 Gang clocked us, whistled out to his crew and started to chase us down.

Through instinct, we both started to run. What was this about?

I keep thinkin - if all the things that happened that night, happened in a different way, Lima would still be with us - and we would b livin our carefree lives still.

Earlier that day Julius and his sister - destroyed the hideout of K9 Gang while they were angry. F the world. No food, no life, no parents. Burned it down cause it was inside them. No one cares about an abandoned warehouse and all the junk inside - right? Until they saw little scraps of burnt paper fly up. Leaflets? Letters?

Money.

Flaming hot money fizzling up into the sky, burning into the air, crisp notes never to be seen again.

Who could have known that K7 would hide their stash in a grimy warehouse, filled with rats and damp wood, strewn across everywhere. Who would have known that Julius' harmless rage would jeopardise so much?

Sister was wearing that same Tottenham Football T shirt that Lima then borrowed from Julius' room that evening.
Someone clocked sister, leavin the scene.

And that's why they followed us on bonfire night.

Julius clocked the chase and tried 2 stay close on our tail - on his bike, trying 2 find us.

Fireworks kept going off and got louder , louder this time.
Come on Julius, find us. Please bro. Come save us.

Akram and his guys were circling, on moped bikes, faces hooded up, now.

Lima stopped, breathless. 'Look. We can try talk it out, K7 got us all wrong. Lets just kill them with kindness. embrace our assailants, so they know we're human.'

Akram jumped off his moped.

'You little queer kids are gonna pay. U gotta pay 4 what u destroyed.' And Akram grabbed us.

So I flicked out my ice pick. Then Akram twisted me into himself, grabbed me - and shoved me toward Lima.

Lima, with his arms open was the most vulnerable. Then my ice pick was gone.

He dropped straight back - and from that memory only, my head breaks down into a million shards of glass.

my bro, my bro, my bro. not my bro Lima.

Julius got there - just 2 minutes too late.

He tried to save us - pulled the icepick out - took it back. But nothing could take back that moment.

Then Julius was standing in the window frame of the warehouse lookin at me. I had him for a second - pls save me bro - then he ran.

Julius kept running, never 2 be seen again in this side of town.

No food, no life, no parents, no Lima.

No lil bro that needs him right now.

Julius didnt see anyone, just kept runnin with my grandad's ice pick.

*

My girl wiped a hot damp cloth over my face.

I had no home anyways so we just laid on her bedroom floor till i stopped shaking.

That night, bonfire night never ended 4 me, fireworks kept bussin off, in the streets and in my head.

123

Timber Road - Back to the hood.

I woke up to a text.

I had 2 go get the ice pick back. My girl looked out the window at the rain- it was a hot day. Hottest day in November.

All the K9 guys from bonfire night were there. I had to find another way - but how?

To even get out of the estate - I'd need to cross the carpark, where they were all standing underneath a K7 Gazebo tent.

I remember seeing an old Mexican film where they used a molotov cocktail 2 trap their enemies in a fire. It was a small gazebo. maybe it could work. Only one way to find out.

Anyways cockroaches survive atomic bombs, so these man would find a way to escape. Eye 4 an eye and all that jazz.

i climbed over the wall to the bike shed - to get Julius's bike. He gave me the keys a while back to unlock it if I ever needed it. Almost as if he saw this afternoon comin.

My girl started 2 get busy chatting with killer Akram from K7.

With perfect timing she looked up and saw me - time to get out of here. She took a few steps back and hopped onto the wall playfully - to distract from what was laying up ahead for K7.

With Lima's face in my mind's eye, I flung the molotov cocktail down, and the glass and the fire spread across the K7 gazebo.

This is 4 you, Lima. Fly in Peace My g.

Me + my girl picked up our bikes and cycled down to the dual carriageway - under the flyover. she grabbed my face with her ringed fingers, all the cold metal from her jewellery soothing the sparks flowing from my body. She tucked her slims arms round underneath my jacket and pulled me close. She smelled like that blueberry hair gel and chewing gum.

I couldnt help thinkin that this is that dual carriageway where me + Lima first played our favourite album - Original Pirate Material by the Streets. Mixed with my memory of that song 'Geezer's Need Excitement'. Right now a geezer could do with some enlightenment - and one more endless afternoon with my broskis. Who knew it could all change like this?

We passed the carpark - and I see me + Julian skateboarding after I got kicked out of my foster home. Seeing Lima rapping and freestyling over the J Dilla beats we found and downloaded.

We kept going and going. my legs werent even mine no more. Had to keep pushing to reach Julius. I remembered to take Silas road instead of Woodland Road - Akram lived there.

I kept going and going - until I felt tears rolling down my face - it felt as if Lima was gonna jump in the pathway of my bicycle.

I cant get u out of my head, g. i cant pass this bit, i wish this place didnt exist.

the warehouse where it all happened.

I had Sevdaliza's ISON Album in my brain - kinda felt like I was glitching or snaking around somehow - like how her voice often did.

my mind cut back 2 that night, bonfire night.

b4 we left, i cut Limas hair - bleached it blonde at the top like mine, and shaved it short on the sides.

but then, seeing him dead, looking so much like me, made me ask my girl 2 just give me a straight up buzz cut.

i hadnt seen me like that in such a long time, since i first transitioned, but i couldn't hold onto Lima's last style.

Silas Road

I could just about make out Julius' face in the dusky evening light. But happiness yawned across me to see him once again. The first person who accepted me and saw me as I was. A yung boi. Not girl, not stud, not lesbian, not a dyke. A yung boi.

'Remember G, that night you told us who you really were. People arent ready for a guy like you -but u dont need to explain urself. Just do you. You'll always be my bro. You'll always be a bro 2 me + Lima.'

I reached my fist out to touch his through the gate that held us from each other. My girl gripped my hand tight, her sharp acrylic nails pressing into my skin.

'I gotta lay low for a bit. Maybe a long time. You already know how it goes. but I aint left u. Lima aint left u.'

He dipped his head low + stuck his fist out. Limas fist came out from the shadows, too.

'We'll always be bros 4 life.'

Remembering Us: An Open Series

For Tom Richardson: poet/painter/pal

by Terrance McLarnan

After all these years,
a lull entered the room
instead of you,
the sun and moon become still.
The light is now unbalanced
shadows land in a different spot
and silence becomes our sound.
Inside this door, life's brutality pulls no punches.
Our solitude will not disappear but
go forward with the kindness of western light
as humanity hums in the background.
Our queries have only begun to ripen.
They hang like hard pears
hidden behind dense leaves
that softened as we wandered;
they left us fat with life,
without remembering much of what was said.
This is the sparest account.
A longer version
does not negate this rendering.
Your necessary departure,
left this old man sadder, if not
sunnier, you are lovelier
than the songbird which brought you.

Ardilla

by Soledad Vargas

When I opened the glass door
I heard the loud yells.
A baby is crying

At first I believed it to be a bird, but
I was proven wrong when I saw its gray lean body.

It hopped through the garden.
It ran across the red pavement.
It continued to cry.
It squeezed itself under the grill like a cat.
It ran towards the rosemary bush.

Where is your protector?
How is it that you are alone?

I continued to hang the white rags on the clothesline
and I heard it's grunts as it attempted to climb the shed.
It saddens me. And it makes me jealous.
How vulnerable, yet how willing to put itself at risk
To be in the open as you seek security.

To go back to sleep when the suns rays
are aimed at another's face.

Where are its protectors?
Are they like my angels?
That look down from the palm tree.
Nestled in between the fronds.
I'm under the category of unfavorable.

Are your angels resting or testing?
When I was done with my task,
I looked behind me in search of the baby.
With my twenty-five years of life, I walk
across the ground towards the glass door.

Betty Crocker is a tough mother—
by Rachel Telljohn

—i am not, okay—

and i want to call my grandmother
how do i get the shortening off my hands?
—except i'm so glad she's dead, and
how awful is that—

i shaft sticks of butter in my bare hands
i think of the guy i'm fucking and—isn't that just the thing
you think something dirty and then you think of your grandma

is this how you did it?
knead molasses straight into the dough, i mean
most of it is honestly on my counter

i've had three separate kitchen counters in California
& i've called her from none of them

i keep thinking if can learn to be some gay housewife
then i'm at least half the woman she was

i keep thinking if i make this dude some bread
then i'm at least avoiding the inevitable

127

just because there are things i would die for
doesn't mean i want to now

is this how she did it?

the dough takes hours to rise, and hours
to rise again and in that time
no one comes and no one died
trying

The Length of a Breeze
by Joseph Imwalle

My father has become a handful of flattened grins
kept around the house for remembrance.

But I have kept for safekeeping, in the folds of my brain,
my father napping beside a river, head resting on his outstretched arm.
Riverbed rocks cover the ground. They are the size of eagle eggs.

The lobe of my brain where he lies is not a lot smaller.

My father is hard to measure. He holds still but my ruler keeps shapeshifting.
I reach for him with a trout. I reach for him with a book, a burger, a beer. I reach
for him with a waxing smile in hand that measures nothing. He is waking from
the nap bemused. I lie beside him in a mirrored position. We feel a sensation
like being an air-mattress love inflated. We consider getting back in the boat but
don't. He is infinitesimally small. He is the size of the sky. He is just out of reach,
about five or six inches. I am five foot nine and alive.

Author Biographies

Kehinde Badiru's poetry books are I Know Why Your Mother Cries (2020) and An Assortment of Poetry Genres (2021). A Candidate of the Creative Writing MFA Program at the St. Mary's College of California, he tweets @Kehindebadiru_ and can be found at kehindebadiru.com.

Kiran Bains Sahota uses storytelling to speak on the cultural realities and generational trauma facing South Asian communities. She received her BA in English from UC Berkeley ('19) and an MFA in Fiction from Saint Mary's College ('21). Her work has been in issues of CollegeMagazine.com, Forum Magazine, Maiden Magazine, as well as her own site, SunsetDahlia.com.

Alison Lubar teaches high school English by day and yoga by night. They are a queer, nonbinary femme of color whose life work (aside from wordsmithing) has evolved into bringing mindfulness practices, and sometimes even poetry, to young people. Their debut chapbook, Philosophers Know Nothing About Love, is forthcoming with Thirty West Publishing in Spring 2022; you can find out more at http://alisonlubar.com/ or on Twitter @theoriginalison.

Molly Montgomery is a writer who lives in the San Francisco Bay Area, where she teaches high school English. Her work has been featured in several literary magazines, including Entropy, X-R-A-Y, and McSweeney's Internet Tendency.

Emily Jewett is a first year nonfiction MFA student at St. Mary's College of California. Her writing deals with themes of trauma and conceptions of womanhood.

Jenny Qi is the author of Focal Point, winner of the 2020 Steel Toe Books Poetry Award. Her essays and poems have been published in The New York Times, The Atlantic, Literary Hub, Tin House, ZYZZYVA, and elsewhere. She grew up mostly in Las Vegas and now lives in San Francisco, where she completed her Ph.D. in Cancer Biology.

Margaret Preigh is a graduate student at Texas A&M University completing her Master's in Science and Technology Journalism. She is a winner of the 2018 Iowa Chapbook Prize in poetry and the 2019 Love of Learning Poetry Prize.

Lauren Camp is the author of five books, most recently Took House (Tupelo Press). Her poems have appeared in Witness, Poet Lore, Kenyon Review, Beloit Poetry Journal, The Los Angeles Review and other journals in the US and abroad. Her poems have been translated into Mandarin, Turkish, Spanish, and Arabic. www.laurencamp.com.

Ryan Buell graduated from Saint Mary's College of California with his Master of Fine Arts in Creative Writing. His visual artwork has appeared in The East Bay Review. He lives in Minneapolis, where he writes and narrates audio description for the blind and visually impaired.

Pınar Banu Yaşar is a Kurdish poet whose work can be found in Tinderbox Poetry Journal, HVTN, and La Bruja Roja. They are an alum of the Tin House SWW, a Brett Elizabeth Jenkins Poetry Prize Finalist, a Poetry Online Launch Prize Finalist, and a Best of the Net Nominee.

Sheila Davies Sumner is a poet and audio artist. She collaborates with visual artist Patrick Sumner, who works with etching, photography, and digital media. Her poems have been published in MARY, Journal of New Writing; Squaw Valley Review; Alcatraz 3; and the graphic-story magazine, one-of-one. She is co-curator, with Casey McAlduff, for the Studio One Reading Series in Oakland.

Mary Cisper's poems and reviews have appeared in Lana Turner, Colorado Review, Newfound, New American Writing, Glint, and elsewhere. Her first collection, "Dark Tussock Moth," won the 2016 Trio Award and was published by Trio House Press (2017).

Jose Hernandez Diaz is a 2017 NEA Poetry Fellow. He is the author of The Fire Eater (Texas Review Press, 2020). He is an editor and educator currently living in Los Angeles County.

Jasmine Kahlia is a multidisciplinary artist from London / Barcelona, with work shown internationally in Spain and USA.

Naihobe Gonzalez is a Venezuelan-American writer in Oakland, California. Her work has appeared in Catapult, The Believer, The Offing, Waxwing, and elsewhere. She holds a Ph.D. in economics from Columbia University and conducts policy research when she's not writing.

Marcie Shlesinger Beyatte writes about mental and physical health, Italian culture and the continual search for home. Her work has been published in The Florentine Magazine, The Toronto Globe and Mail, Contra Costa Times, Verbsap and other journals and anthologies.

Cintia Santana teaches fiction and poetry workshops in Spanish, as well as literary translation courses at Stanford University. A recipient of Djerassi and CantoMundo fellowships, her work has appeared in Best New Poets 2020, Beloit Poetry Journal, Guernica, The Iowa Review, Kenyon Review, Pleiades, Poetry Northwest, The Threepenny Review, West Branch, and other journals. Her first poetry collection, The Disordered Alphabet, is forthcoming from Four Way Books. To learn more go to: www.cintiasantana.com.

Maya Alexandria is a biracial African American writer, painter, poet, and filmmaker in California. She is the Chief Marketing Officer and Producer of Mad Mouth Poetry Inc. Maya is currently completing NYU's film program while traveling around California to perform featured readings.

Simone Muench is the author of Orange Crush (Sarabande), Wolf Centos (Sarabande), and Suture (Black Lawrence), a sonnet collection written with Dean Rader. Most recently, she co-edited They Said: A Multi-Genre Anthology of Contemporary Collaborative Writing (Black Lawrence). She is a professor at Lewis

University where she is the faculty advisor for Jet Fuel Review. She also serves as a senior poetry editor for Tupelo Quarterly and poetry editor for Jackleg Press.

Jackie K. White, former professor at Lewis University and faculty advisor for Jet Fuel Review, has published several chapbooks and served as an assistant editor for the collaborative anthology, They Said. Her collaborative chapbook, Hex & Howl, co-written with Simone Muench, is forthcoming from Black Lawrence Press, 2021.

Maw Shein Win is a poet, editor, and educator who lives and teaches in the Bay Area. Her poetry chapbooks are Ruins of a glittering palace (SPA/Commonwealth Projects) and Score and Bone (Nomadic Press). Invisible Gifts: Poems was published by Manic D Press in 2018. Her full-length poetry collection is Storage Unit for the Spirit House (Omnidawn, 2020), longlisted for the 2021 PEN America Open Book Award. Mawsheinwin.com.

Carol Dorf has three chapbooks available, "Given," (Origami Poems,) "Some Years Ask," (Moria Press) and "Theory Headed Dragon," (Finishing Line Press). Her poetry appears in "Shofar," "About Place," "Great Weather For Media," "Slipstream," "The Mom Egg," "Sin Fronteras," "Heresies," "Feminist Studies," "Scientific American," and "Maintenant." She was founding poetry editor of Talking Writing.

Lily Darling published her first novel, Southing, in December 2019. Her poem "self-portrait as the mirror who shows every face but my own (embarrassing, I know)" won the 2021 Ramon Feliciano Poetry Prize, sponsored by the Academy of American Poets. She is currently the Co-Editor-in-Chief of the literary journal Laurel Moon. She lives in Brooklyn, New York.

Rusty Morrison is co-publisher of Omnidawn (www.omnidawn.com). Her five books include After Urgency (won Tupelo's Dorset Prize) & the true keeps calm biding its story (won Ahsahta's Sawtooth Prize, James Laughlin Award, N.California Book Award, & DiCastagnola Award). Her recent Beyond the Chainlink was a finalist for the NCIB Award & NCB Award). She teaches & she gives writing consultations. Her website: www.rustymorrison.com.

Matthew Brailas received his MFA in poetry from NYU. He lives and works in New Haven. His work has previously appeared or is forthcoming in Foothill Journal, The St. Ann's Review, FILTH, Pigeon Pages, Spoon River Poetry Review, The Carolina Quarterly, The Washington Square Review, and elsewhere.

Loisa Fenichell's work has been nominated for a Pushcart Prize and Best of the Net and has been featured or is forthcoming in Guernica Magazine, Tupelo Quarterly, Washington Square Review, Narrative Magazine, Poetry Northwest, and elsewhere. Her debut chapbook, "all these urban fields," was published by nothing to say press. She is currently an MFA candidate at Columbia University.

Lisa Ludden is the author of the chapbook Palebound (Flutter Press, 2017). Winner of SF Litquake's 2019 Writing Contest, her poems have appeared in Interim, The Normal School, Epiphany, and elsewhere. She holds an MFA from Saint

Mary's College of California and a BA in English from San Francisco State University. She lives in the San Francisco Bay Area with her family.

Leora Fridman is author of My Fault, selected by Eileen Myles for the Cleveland State University Press First Book Prize, in addition to other books of prose, poetry and translation. Recent work has appeared in Full Stop, the New York Times, and Triangle House, among others, and Fridman's work has been supported by organizations including Fulbright, the NEA and the Andy Warhol Foundation.

Brandy Collins is a writer living in the Bay Area. Brandy is a 2019-2020 cohort graduate from the Maynard Institute for Journalism, a correspondent for Oakland Voices, and contributing writer for Oaklandside, Berkeleyside-Nosh and SF Weekly.

Julie L. Moore is the author of four poetry collections, including, most recently, Full Worm Moon, which won a 2018 Woodrow Hall Top Shelf Award and received honorable mention for the Conference on Christianity and Literature's 2018 Book of the Year Award. Her poetry has appeared in many anthologies and journals. She is the Writing Center Director at Taylor University, where she is also the poetry editor for Relief Journal. julielmoore.com.

Jules Henderson received her MFA in Writing from the University of San Francisco. Her writing has been published in The Bookends Review, The Social Poet, Paradise Review, Words Fly Away: Poems for Fukushima, and Hitched!: Wedding Stories from San Francisco City Hall. Instagram: thejulestheory.

JoAnn Scandiffio is an educator and a gemologist living in San Francisco. Her work has appeared in Calyx, The Poeming Pigeon, Poets 11 2016, Masques & Spectacle, Switched-on Gutenberg, Sugared Water, Naugatuck Review.

Siavash Saadlou is a writer and literary translator whose works of fiction, creative nonfiction, and criticism have appeared in Plenitude Magazine, The Southeast Review, and Minor Literature[s]. His poetry has been anthologized in Essential Voices: Poetry of Iran and Its Diaspora (Green Linden Press, 2021), and his translations are available in Denver Quarterly, The Los Angeles Review, and Asymptote, among other journals. Saadlou holds an MFA in creative writing from Saint Mary's College of California.

CAConrad has been working with the ancient technologies of poetry and ritual since 1975. They are the author of AMANDA PARADISE: Resurrect Extinct Vibration (Wave Books, 2021). Other titles include While Standing in Line for Death and Ecodeviance. They received a Creative Capital grant, a Pew Fellowship, a Lambda Literary Award, and a Believer Magazine Book Award. They teach at Columbia University in New York City and Sandberg Art Institute in Amsterdam.

Alan Saint Clark is your friendly neighborhood Supervillain, ontological mechanic, and founder of Phantom Electrik Comics. To join in our cause visit Phantomelectrik.com and consume.

132

Carol Moldaw's fifth collection of poems, Beauty Refracted, appeared in 2018 (Four Way Books). Her work has been published widely in journals, including The New York Review of Books, Poem-A- Day, AGNI, FIELD, Harvard Review, Yale Review and The New Yorker. She lives in Santa Fe, New Mexico, and teaches privately.

Ellen Kombiyil is the author of Histories of the Future Perfect (2015), and a micro chapbook Avalanche Tunnel (2016). Recent work has appeared or is forthcoming in The Minnesota Review, New Ohio Review, North American Review, Ploughshares, and Salt Hill. She co-founded The (Great) Indian Poetry Collective, a mentorship-model press publishing emerging poets from India and the diaspora, and currently teaches creative writing at Hunter College.

Krista Varela Posell is a queer Latina writer living in San Francisco. She received her MFA in Creative Writing from Saint Mary's College in 2014 and her essays have appeared in Brevity, The Coachella Review, and elsewhere. She can be found tweeting and 'gramming @kdvarela84.

Jamey Gallagher lives in Baltimore. He teaches writing at the Community College of Baltimore County.

Jenny Mitchell is winner of the Poetry Book Awards 2021 for her second collection Map of a Plantation, also a Poet's Recommendation 2021 (Poetry Society). She's won eleven other competitions. A debut collection, Her Lost Language, is joint winner of the Geoff Stevens Memorial Poetry Prize and was voted One of 44 Books of 2019 (Poetry Wales). She's an Artist in Association at the University of London and currently working on her third collection.

Terrance McLarnan is an artist, poet and psychoanalyst (in that order). He studied photography at the Minneapolis College of Art and Design and has produced black and white photographs for over 40 years. His work is in the permanent collection of the Plains Art Museum as well as in private collections. His poetry has been published in Psychoanalytic Perspectives and its' anthology, Creative Writings from the Moon Poetry by Psychoanalyst and Others and recently in the journal fort da.

Jo'kia Mc Call was born and raised in Oakland, California. She is a mother to 4 year old and a preschool teacher.

Shelley Walden has a B.A. in Journalism and International Studies from the University of North Carolina at Chapel Hill. Her writing has appeared in numerous publications, including USA Today, Foreign Policy in Focus, Cricket, Spider, the Chapel Hill Herald and Twiniversity, among others. She lives in New Mexico with her husband and twins.

Jennifer Sapio was born and raised in Austin, Texas. She is currently pursuing an MFA from New York University in Creative Writing. You can see her publications at Medium, The Write Launch, Sonder Midwest, Raw Art Review, Chattahoochee Review, jennisapio.com, and elsewhere. She also volunteers for the Inside Literature program at the Travis County Correctional Complex and the Girls Empowerment Network.

Anne H. Putnam is a teacher, writer, and editor living in northwest Washington – her first memoir, Navel Gazing, was published in the UK in 2013 by Faber&Faber. She is currently revising her second memoir and working on a novel. Anne primarily writes about relationships (especially heartbreak/healing), body image, and mental health.

Klein Voorhees (them/them) is a poet, artist, and translator from North Carolina. They are currently pursuing their M.F.A in Creative Writing at California College of the Arts. You can find their work in publications such as Asymptote Journal, perhappened, and Monstering Magazine, or on their website: www.kleinvoorhees.com.

Cy Ozgood is often in between.

Valerie Wong (AKA @theglutenfreepoet on Instagram) was born in Toronto, grew up in Hong Kong and is currently working as a management consultant in New York. As a Third Culture Kid (TCK), she is at once a local and a foreigner wherever she goes.

Kathleen Winter is the author of Transformer, I will not kick my friends, and Nostalgia for the Criminal Past. Her chapbook Cat's Tongue will be published in 2022. Her poems and fiction have appeared in The New Republic, The New Statesman, Michigan Quarterly Review, Five Points, and Cincinnati Review. Winter's awards include the Poetry Society of America The Writer Magazine/ Emily Dickinson Award, fellowships to the Dora Maar House and James Merrill House, and the Ralph Johnston Fellowship.

Kathryn Jordan hails from Berkeley, CA. Two of her poems won Honorable Mention for this year's Steve Kowit Poetry Prize, two poems awarded Special Merit for the Muriel Craft Bailey Prize, and another is a finalist for the Patricia Dobler Poetry Award. Kathryn is the recipient of the San Miguel de Allende Poetry Prize and the Sidney Lanier Poetry Award. Her poems can be found at The Sun, New Ohio Review, and the Atlanta Review. http://kathrynjordan.org/

L. A. Johnson is from California. She is the author of the chapbook Little Climates (Bull City Press, 2017). She is currently pursuing her PhD in literature and creative writing from the University of Southern California. Her poems have recently appeared or are forthcoming in The American Poetry Review, Best New Poets, Missouri Review, Prairie Schooner, The Southern Review, ZYZZYVA, and other journals. Find her online at http://www.la-johnson.com.

Dakota Valdez received her BA in English from St. Mary's College of California. She enjoys writing poetry and memoir. Dakota is a high school English teacher in the Bay Area, as well as a local artist. She is currently pursuing her MFA in Poetry at Saint Marys. Her work is featured in the upcoming poetry anthology, Looys: Voices of Resistance in Verse.

Cynthia Randolph is an artist and writer who works across photography, video, poetry, and creative nonfiction. She has exhibited throughout the United States and abroad. Her writing has been published in Canvas, Omniverse, Written Here (and There), Community of Writers Poetry Review. She lives in San Francisco where in addition to her writing and art practices she works as a Crisis Counselor and is a practitioner of Sōtō Zen Buddhism.

Natascha Graham is a writer of stage and screen as well as of fiction and poetry. She lives with her wife in a house full of sunshine on the east coast of England. Her poetry, fiction and non-fiction essays have been previously published by Acumen, Litro, Every Day Fiction, The Sheepshead Review, Yahoo News and The Mighty. Natascha also has an upcoming poetry pamphlet published with Tall Lighthouse in 2021 and writes a continuing radio drama for BBC Radio Suffolk.

Cara Meredith is a freelance writer, speaker and conversationalist. A former high school English teacher and non-profit outreach director, her first book, The Color of Life: A Journey Toward Love and Racial Justice (Zondervan 2019), is a spiritual memoir about her journey as a white woman into issues of race. She lives with her family in Oakland, California.

The Rev. **Elizabeth Riley** is a priest in the Episcopal Church. She was born and raised in Alaska before attending Saint Mary's College of California for her undergraduate studies in theology. She was ordained a priest in 2013. She currently lives on Mercer Island in Washington with her husband and three children.

Stella Santamaría is the daughter of a Cuban exile and a Guatemalan immigrant. Stella holds an MFA in Creative Writing from Saint Mary's College of California, recipient of the SOLA Dean's Award. Her poetry has been recently published in The Acentos Review, Juked, and Nine Mile Magazine. Santamaría is the Sandra Cisneros Fellow at Under the Volcano 2021 and an alumna of the Community of Writers. She lives in Miami.

Tina Cane is Poet Laureate of Rhode Island, the founder/ director of Writers-in-the-Schools, RI, and the author of Dear Elena: Letters for Elena Ferrante, Once More With Feeling, Body of Work, and Year of the Murder Hornet (Veliz Books). She was a 2020 Poet Laureate Fellow with the Academy of American Poets and is the creator/ curator of the distance reading series, Poetry is Bread. Her YA novel-in-verse, Alma Presses Play, was released in 2021.

Edith Friedman's work has appeared or is forthcoming in Sisyphus Literary Magazine, Zingara Poetry Review, The Ekphrastic Review and Epoch Literary Journal. She is an MFA student at Saint Mary's College of California.

Rachel Telljohn is a recent poetry graduate of the MFA program at Saint Mary's College. She currently lives and writes in Kansas, with her cat Matilda and her best friend from SMC.

Soledad Vargas is a first generation native Californian who is currently studying for an M.F.A. in Creative Writing at Saint Mary's College of California. She received a B.A in communication studies from the California state University, Stanislaus. As a daughter of Mexican immigrants, her writing is influenced by Michoacán culture, spirituality, and music.

Bixby Jane is an adopted Angeleno, observing of the passing, gatherer of words.

Sage received their MFA in Creative Writing from Saint Mary's College of California. Their poems have appeared in North American Review, The Rumpus, Pittsburgh Poetry Review, Penn Review, Drunk Monkeys, and elsewhere. They live in Kansas.

AJ Strosahl is a writer who lives and works in Oakland, California. She holds an MFA from St. Mary's College of California and her work can be found or is forthcoming in The Summerset Review, Oyster River Pages, Signal Mountain Review, and other outlets. In 2022, AJ will be the fall artist in residence at the Bryn Du Art Center.

Natalie Dunn is a writer and editor currently living in Berkeley. Her work has been published or is forthcoming in Conduit, The Believer, The Rumpus, RHINO, The Kenyon Review, and elsewhere. She is at work on her debut novel and a collection of poems.

Megan Noble grew up in the East Bay, studied English at UC Berkeley, and is now a Teaching Fellow and MFA Candidate in Creative Writing Nonfiction at Saint Mary's College of California. A hardcore Swiftie, she still thinks reputation should've won a Grammy.

Heather June Gibbons is the author of Her Mouth As Souvenir (University of Utah Press), winner of the Agha Shahid Ali Poetry Prize, and a finalist for the Northern California Book Award. Her poems have appeared in Best New Poets, Blackbird, Boston Review, Drunken Boat, Gulf Coast, Indiana Review, jubilat and New American Writing, among others. She lives in San Francisco, CA.

Originally from San Francisco, **Tongo Eisen-Martin** is a poet, movement worker, and educator. His latest curriculum on extrajudicial killing of Black people, We Charge Genocide Again, has been used as an educational and organizing tool throughout the country. His latest book "Blood On The Fog" was released this fall in the City Lights Pocket Poets series. He is San Francisco's eighth poet laureate.

Jo Unruh is just happy to be here.

Joey Patterson was born and raised in Dublin, California. After a few years in aquatics, Joey began pursuing a career in writing. He recently graduated from Saint Mary's College of California with an MFA in Nonfiction while also teaching writing circles at the school's writing center.

Marilyn Abildskov is the author of The Men in My Country. Her essays and short stories have been published in Ploughshares, Sewanee Review, Crazyhorse, Southern Review, Best American Essays, and elsewhere. She currently holds the

Olivia Filippi Chair in Creative Writing at Saint Mary's College of California where she teaches in the MFA Program.

Samantha Weiland is an Oregon native. She received her BA in English with an emphasis in Creative Writing from Saint Mary's College of California, and is currently studying to earn a MFA in Creative Writing, also from Saint Mary's.

Daisy He migrated from Shanghai, China to the United States in 2019, the year in which she started to write in English. She holds an MFA in Creative Nonfiction from Saint Mary's College of California. She currently lives in Moraga, California.

Christine Hyung-Oak Lee is the author of the memoir Tell Me Everything You Don't Remember, which was featured in The New York Times, Self Magazine, Time Magazine, and NPR's Weekend Edition with Scott Simon. She lives in Berkeley with chickens and bees.

Jacqueline Hughes Simon's writing has appeared in the Cal Literature & Arts Magazine, The Cortland Review, Okay Donkey, Boaat Journal, Pennsylvania English, Pine Hills Review and the anthology Ode to My Undoing (Risk Press). She was nominated for Best of the Net by Okay Donkey in 2020. In 2021 Jacqueline received her Master of Fine Arts in poetry from Saint Mary's College of California. She is a volunteer and board member of an environmental education nonprofit, where she works with and trains donkeys.

Joe Imwalle received his MFA in Poetry from St Mary's College of CA. He lives in Oakland with his wife and daughter where he teaches Spanish online and enjoys finding the horizon with his bicycle. He's working on a translation project and a debut book of poems. His work can be found in Beyond Words, Indolent Books: What Rough Beast, The Courtship of Winds, and No Contact Mag.

Ada Limón is the author of six books of poetry, including The Carrying, which won the National Book Critics Circle Award for Poetry. Limón is also the host of the critically-acclaimed poetry podcast, The Slowdown.

Kailyn McCord lives in Fort Bragg, CA. Her work appears in Ploughshares, Literary Hub, Brevity, The Believer, The Cincinnati Review, Alta Magazine, and Pleiades, among others. With support from the Bread Loaf Writers' Conference and the Ucross Foundation, Kailyn writes about California, fire, addiction, and love. In 2022, Kailyn will attend the Margery Davis Boyden Wilderness Writing Residency, where there is no internet, cell service, or electricity. When not writing, she likes to go camping.

This book was set in 10 point Palatino Linotype
Designed by Charlie Pendergast and Kevin Connor
Printed in the United States